FUN WITH STUNTS

Fun With Stunts

by

EFFA E. PRESTON

A Collection of Short Skits, Sketches, Stunts, Games, Pantomimes, Charades, Action and Musical Novelties, Entertainments, and Talking Acts. Written for presentation by teen-agers and adults for the entertainment of audiences and participants.

Publishers

T. S. DENISON & COMPANY
MINNEAPOLIS, MINNESOTA

Printed in the U.S.A.
By The Brings Press

International Copyright Secured

Library of Congress Catalog Card Number: 56-12136

PRODUCTION RIGHTS

Foreword

For many years I have been a member of various clubs and groups continually having social gatherings. At times I have been the chairman of the entertainment committee. Therefore, I am fully aware of the difficulties encountered in providing simple but satisfactory amusements for such occasions.

In any large gathering, there are always wallflowers, very shy or unsocial people, strangers, or reserved and over-dignified souls. Even worse, sometimes there are guests of honor who must be entertained and not bored.

There is seldom, if ever, a large party at which all the guests dance or play cards. People, no matter how talkative they may be, get weary if they just sit and talk for the entire afternoon or evening. I felt that something should be done to relieve the monotony and add zest to the occasion. But what?

And then I thought of my grandmother's gay stories of the parties she attended when she was a girl, and how everyone enjoyed doing stunts, mental or physical. I determined to try the stunt method myself. I found it worked admirably.

Children could usually be launched on a good time by games, but they needed some new ones. I invented some games and stunts and tried them out at a school party, as I was teaching a primary grade at the time. The children liked most of the games; those they were not enthusiastic about I eliminated from my list.

Encouraged by this small beginning I decided to do something for the mature groups whose parties I shared. I planned to write a book of stunts. I felt that, whatever else they were, the stunts must be simple and require no staging, no rehearsals, no favorite players. Everyone must be, in turn, a part of the act. I wrote a few short skits and then concentrated on stunts, suitable for any gathering and not requiring much effort or imagination on the part of the players. To quote Shelley, most of us have "as much imagination as a pint jar."

The stunts, sketches and skits were tried out at club meetings and parties by people who were not shy and who loved to entertain. The material received most enthusiastically was retained for later use; the rest was thrown out.

Then I re-tested all the material I had assembled; tested it by the hard but only authentic manner, production by unrehearsed participants before an impartial and rather skeptical audience. After this I wrote down in detail all the skits, stunts, pantomimes and anything else that had proved really popular and put them in my book.

I hope my stunts serve as "ice breakers" and help to change gloomy gatherings into gay parties. Try out the stunts and if the first one you do isn't a smash hit try another, but keep on trying. Remember there is nothing more dreary and depressing to both guests and hostess, to chairman and committee members, than a party or a social affair at which the people sit about looking "grand, gloomy, and peculiar," as a historian said of Napoleon.

Chase away their gloom and delusions of grandeur. If they are show-offs give them an opportunity to display their gifts. If they are timid souls and have some latent talent, make them drag it out of hiding. In short, try stunts. You may be surprised at the result. Here's luck to you!

—Effa E. Preston

Contents

SECTION ONE — *Skits and Sketches*

SECTION TWO — *Stunts For All Occasions*

SECTION THREE — *Action and Musical Stunts*

SECTION FOUR — *Pantomimes and Charades*

SECTION FIVE — *Games For All Occasions*

11

Section One
Skits and Sketches

THE AFTERNOON OF OCTOBER TWENTIETH

(A courtroom farce)

FOR TWELVE MEN AND THREE WOMEN, OR ALL MEN

CHARACTERS

CLERK OF THE COURT, *who hates everybody, especially people*

MR. BROWN
MR. JONES
MR. SMITH
MR. MARTIN
} *spectators at the trial*

JUDGE BENZEDRENE BLUFFINGWELL, *dignified and disagreeable*

COUNSELLOR GETEMOFF, *attorney for the plaintiff, sweet and sympathetic*

DISTRICT ATTORNEY SENDEMUP, *blustering and mean*

MATT MORTIMER, *the defendant, a well-meaning but confused young man*

VIOLET VALE, *the young and pretty plaintiff, born in a daze*

MR. BLAKE
MR. DRAKE
} *witnesses for the defense*

MISS EMMA TEABALL
MISS LUCY LOCKETT
} *fuzzy witnesses for the plaintiff*

FOREMAN OF THE JURY

ELEVEN JURORS

SCENE: JUDGE BLUFFINGWELL'S *courtroom. Entrances are at right and left. At center is the* JUDGE'S *bench, at right of which are two rows of chairs facing front, for the jury. At left are chairs for the spectators. Near the* Judge's *bench at left is the witness stand, a chair on a low platform. Down right are tables and chairs for the lawyers and chairs for the plaintiff, defendant, and witnesses. The clerk's desk and chair are at right, close to the* Judge's *chair. On the wall at back are large posters reading:* "Cut-rate Divorces," "Judge Benzedrine Bluffingwell," "Visit Our County Jail," *and* "If You Have Troubles, Come In. We'll Double 'Em."

At the rise of the curtain, the Clerk *is alone on the stage, sitting at his desk reading a comic book. He looks at his watch, puts the book in his pocket, takes a duster from his pocket, and begins to dust the* Judge's *chair.*

Clerk. People! They make me sick. Always getting into trouble. It's a good thing I'm not the judge; I'd send 'em all to jail for life. (*Stops dusting and sits to read comic book again.*) I don't even have time to keep up with my reading. (*Hears talking off right.*) Gosh-darned people! Rushing to trials as if this court was a circus; not that Ringling Brothers couldn't learn a lot from us. (*Puts comic book sadly in the desk.*) Now I'll have to wait to see what happened to Blondie. (*Goes off right.*)

Messrs. Brown, Jones, Smith, *and* Martin *enter at left and take seats at left.*

Jones. This trial oughta be good. Auto accident— Violet Vale versus Matt Mortimer.
Smith. I don't know which is worse—the traffic or the new traffic regulations. By the time we learn which

streets to go up, they change the rules, and we have to go down 'em. I find it all very confusing.

JONES. You're right. Every week I vow I'll quit driving a car; but I keep right on. All courage and no brain—that's me.

EMMA TEABALL *and* LUCY LOCKETT *enter at left, cross and sit at right. The four men whistle at them. The women pay no attention, but fix their make-up. They look weary and disheveled.*

LUCY (*breathlessly*). Those terrible buses! They might have sent a station wagon for us—a police-station wagon, I mean. If the bus line only wouldn't change the stops all the time. You never know where you're going or how. Last week I started for the railroad station and landed at the graveyard.

EMMA. And the buses are so crowded you need a buttered shoehorn to get on one at all. Packed in like sardines! Elbows in your face!

LUCY. Something ought to be done about it. I always say an ounce of prevention is worth a sock in the jaw.

EMMA. The Public Service Company ought to give a group hospital policy with every fare.

LUCY. I have an idea. The bus driver could number off the passengers and then make the even numbers breathe in while the odd numbers breathe out. Just think what that would do for that nice Mrs. Morgan— you know—the fat one. She always tries to work her way to the back of the bus going sideways; and the poor thing hasn't any sideways.

EMMA (*changing the subject*). I'm so proud to be a witness for Violet. If she wins a lot of money, she's going to throw a big party.

LUCY. Violet's so sweet. You feel sticky after you've talked to her for an hour. She's my very dearest friend.

EMMA. Sometimes I think she's just a little—er—odd—but—

LUCY. I always say it's all right to be odd if you're rich or famous. Otherwise, you get put into an institution. Emma, what questions do you think they'll ask us?

EMMA. It's the answers I'm worried about. I'm suspicious of that prosecutor—what's his name?—Sendemup.

LUCY. I always say if you're suspicious of everybody, ten times out of nine you're right.

The four MEN *have been listening to this conversation with interest. The* JURY, LAWYERS, *and* VIOLET VALE *enter at right and take their seats.* VIOLET *holds her right arm stiffly, as if it were crippled. The* CLERK *enters at right.*

CLERK. Hear ye, hear ye! Court is now in session. Rise for his Honor, Judge Benzedrine Bluffingwell.

All rise. JUDGE BLUFFINGWELL *stalks on at right, waves a careless hand at the audience, seats himself and glares at everybody. All sit.*

CLERK. Judge, your bull pup chewed up the court bible.

JUDGE. Well, make the witnesses kiss the pup. We can't adjourn to get a new bible.

CLERK (*taking the bible from his pocket and holding it up*). I won't have to do that, Judge. I borrowed a bible from the cleaning woman.

JUDGE (*pounding on desk with gavel*). The case of

Vale versus Mortimer is now opened. Violet Vale and
Matt Mortimer, stand up and give the jury a treat.
(VIOLET *and* MATT *stand for a moment. One juryman
whistles and is glared at by the* FOREMAN. VIOLET *and*
MATT *sit.*) Attorney Sendemup, begin. I've got a golf
game after this.

SENDEMUP (*swaggering to front*). Your Honor and
gentlemen of the jury, I shall prove to you that on the
afternoon of October twentieth the fair plaintiff, Miss
Violet Vale, was crossing the street at the intersection
of Bayard and George with her friends, Miss Emma
Teaball and Miss Lucy Lockett, when suddenly and
without any warning whatsoever, the defendant, Matt
Mortimer, driving sixty-one miles an hour, came down
Bayard Street and struck the plaintiff, causing her
severe injury and putting a permanent kink in her nerves
and one arm.

GETEMOFF (*rising and coming to front*). Your
Honor and gentlemen of the jury, I shall prove that
everything my distinguished opponent is about to prove
is not true. In the first place, there wasn't any accident. In the second place, if there was an accident, my
client wasn't there. If he was there, it wasn't his car.
If it was his car, he was driving only ten miles an hour.
If he did hit a woman, he didn't hurt her, and—and
anyway he wasn't there. (*Sits as the men witnesses
applaud.*)

SENDEMUP (*to* CLERK). Call Miss Lucy Lockett.

CLERK. Miss Lucy Lockett, take the stand. (*She
does.*) Raise your right hand. (*She does.*) Do you
blah-blah-blah-blah?

LUCY (*touching the bible with her left hand as the
CLERK holds it out*). I do.

SENDEMUP. Miss Lockett, you do know the nature
of an oath?

LUCY (*cheerfully*). Oh, yes, .sir. If I swear to a lie, I've got to stick to it.

SENDEMUP (*flustered*). Er—well, Miss Lockett—you may—er—be excused till later.

LUCY (*disappointed*). Doesn't anybody want to ask me any questions? (*Looks around eagerly.*) I know a lot of answers.

SENDEMUP, GETEMOFF, and JUDGE (*in concert*). No, thank you.

(LUCY *sits, feeling slighted.*)

SENDEMUP (*to* CLERK). Call Miss Emma Teaball.

CLERK. Miss Emma Teaball, please take the stand. (EMMA *sits in the witness's chair.*) Raise your right hand. (*She raises it.*) Do you blah-blah-blah-blah?

EMMA (*touching book*). Yes, of course.

SENDEMUP. Miss Teaball, do you know the defendant?

EMMA (*looking* MATT *over coldly*). His face looks simple, but I have no memory for names.

SENDEMUP. Were you with Miss Vale when this sad accident happened?

EMMA. I certainly was, and so was Lucy Lockett.

SENDEMUP. Miss Teaball, tell the jury in your own words just what happened then.

EMMA (*surprised*). Don't you want me to say what we practiced last night?

VIOLET. Oh, dear!

(BLAKE *and* DRAKE *laugh.*)

SENDEMUP (*hastily*). Just tell what happened, Miss Teaball, just—er—just as you remember it.

EMMA (*enjoying herself*). Well, it was like this.

Violet and I were hurrying to get to the football game. Not that I care for ball games; they're so cruel. Somebody's always kicking a goal—poor thing! But we didn't want to miss any excitement. We wouldn't have, either, because I heard later that, up to then, I mean up to when the accident happened, the score was nothing to nothing. Well, we were crossing Bayard Street when that—that—madman driving like a bat out of h—er—the bad place—tore down Bayard Street and hit poor dear Violet. He went right on and left her lying there. There wasn't another soul in sight except those two men. (*Points to* BLAKE *and* DRAKE.) They came running up, just to get their names in the paper.

SENDEMUP (*to jury*). You see? It's very plain. Your witness, Mr. Getemoff. (*Sits.*)

GETEMOFF (*coming to the front and speaking sweetly*). Miss Teaball, was the traffic light green when you—er—crossed Bayard Street?

EMMA. Why—I don't remember— (*Brightly.*) But it must have been the right color, or we wouldn't have crossed.

GETEMOFF. Of course, Miss Teaball, of course. Do you drive a car, Miss Teaball?

EMMA. In an advisory capacity only.

GETEMOFF. Ah, a back-seat driver. (*Abruptly.*) Miss Teaball, you are under oath, remember. Did Matt Mortimer's car hit Violet Vale?

EMMA (*sarcastically*). Oh, no. Mr. Mortimer leaned out and bit her as he drove by.

(*Everybody but* BLAKE *and* DRAKE, JUDGE, *and* GETEMOFF *laughs heartily.* GETEMOFF *motions to* EMMA *to sit. She does.*)

GETEMOFF (*to* CLERK). Call James Drake.

CLERK. James Drake, take the stand. (DRAKE *does*.) Raise your right hand. (*He does*.) Do you blah-blah-blah-blah?

DRAKE (*touching book*). I do.

GETEMOFF. Mr. Drake, did you see this accident?

DRAKE. Yes, sir. I did.

GETEMOFF. Tell the jury exactly what happened.

DRAKE. Matt was driving about twenty miles an hour down Bayard—or—or was it Patterson Street? Anyway, it was whichever one you could come out of but not enter that day. Miss Vale—the good-looking dame with the lame arm—(*pointing*) was crossing the street with the two dames sitting over there. (*He points*.) And they sorta bumped into each other. Matt had the right of way. That's all.

GETEMOFF. Thank you, Mr. Drake. (*To* SENDEMUP.) Your witness.

SENDEMUP. Mr. Drake, are you a friend of the defendant?

DRAKE. Yes, sir.

SENDEMUP. Do you consider him a young man of—er—ordinary intelligence?

DRAKE. Brother, Matt Mortimer could find a needle in a haystack and thread it with a camel.

SENDEMUP. You are sure he is not a careless driver?

DRAKE. He isn't a worm-style motorist, if that's what you mean.

SENDEMUP. And just what is a worm-style motorist, Mr. Drake?

DRAKE (*pleased with himself*). You know: A worm never gives a signal which way it'll turn.

SENDEMUP (*annoyed*). Mr. Drake, what is your opinion of traffic conditions in—(*names town*) from the viewpoint of a pedestrian?

DRAKE. Terrible. Every time I cross the street I

keep halfway between Oh Lord and Thank God. But I
still say Matt is a careful driver.

SENDEMUP. That's all, Mr. Drake. (DRAKE *sits*.)

GETEMOFF (*to* CLERK). Call Bertram Blake.

CLERK. Mr. Bertram Blake, take the stand. (BLAKE
sits in the witness chair.) Raise your right hand. (*He
does*.) Do you blah-blah-blah-blah?

BLAKE (*touching book*). I do.

GETEMOFF. Mr. Blake, is it true that the plaintiff
was crossing the street when she should have been standing on the corner waiting for the light to change?

BLAKE. Yep.

GETEMOFF. Your witness, Mr. Sendemup.

SENDEMUP. Mr. Blake, have you ever appeared as a
witness before?

BLAKE. Yep.

SENDEMUP. What suit?

BLAKE. My blue serge.

SENDEMUP. Mr. Blake, please try to understand
what I ask you. Did you see Matt Mortimer hit Miss
Vale?

BLAKE. Yep.

SENDEMUP (*pleased*). A-ah!

BLAKE. That is, I saw the accident, but Matt really
didn't hit her. Miss Vale walked right into Matt's car.
She wasn't looking where she was going.

SENDEMUP. Is it true, Mr. Blake, that you called to
the defendant, "Don't worry, Matt. It wasn't your
fault"?

BLAKE. Yep.

SENDEMUP. It was none of your business. Even you
must see that.

BLAKE. Yep, but it makes business so limited if you
just stick to your own.

SENDEMUP (*disgusted*). That's all. (*Pleased with*

himself, BLAKE *resumes his seat.* SENDEMUP *turns to
the* CLERK.)   Call Matt Mortimer.

CLERK.   Mr. Matt Mortimer, take the stand. (MATT
MORTIMER *sits in the witness chair.*)   Raise your right
hand. (*He does.*) Do you blah-blah-blah-blah?

MATT (*touching the book*). Blah—er—I mean I do.

SENDEMUP. Now, Mr. Mortimer, where were you on
the afternoon of October twentieth? At exactly two-
thirty o'clock?

MATT. Er—driving down Bayard Street.

SENDEMUP (*sternly*). Why did you not blow your
horn when you saw three ladies crossing the street?
Why didn't you stop for the plaintiff?

MATT. I didn't know she was the plaintiff then, or
I would have.

SENDEMUP (*bellowing*). Why didn't you give the
lady half the street?

MATT. I couldn't find out which half she wanted.

SENDEMUP. Mr. Mortimer, what model is your car?

MATT. It's not a model. It's a horrible example. I
bought it from your brother.

(*The jury laugh loudly.*)

SENDEMUP. Why didn't you stop when you hit
somebody?

MATT. I didn't hit her. She just thinks I did.

SENDEMUP. Didn't you knock down a man on Albany
Street last month?

MATT. I didn't knock him down. I pulled up to let
him go across, and he fainted—from surprise.

SENDEMUP. Do you mean to say you never had an
accident before?

MATT. No, sir—I mean, yes, sir.

SENDEMUP. Isn't it true that last June you turned

a corner when there wasn't any corner and smashed a truck?

LUCY (*loudly*). Any time the road turns when he does, it's just a coincidence.

CLERK. Sh-h!

SENDEMUP. Answer my question, Mr. Mortimer.

MATT. It musta been two other fellows, sir.

SENDEMUP. Are you sure it wasn't your blue road-ster that ran into a green sedan at 4:57 the after-noon of August third, on the Easton Avenue bridge?

MATT (*weakly*). Since you've been asking me so many questions, I'm not even sure I have a car.

(SENDEMUP *sits, shaking his head in despair.* GET-EMOFF *comes to down center.*)

GETEMOFF. Just one more question, Mr. Mortimer. When you admitted that you drove down Bayard Street on the day in question, were you not confusing the streets? Didn't you really mean you drove down Pat-terson Street?

MATT. Maybe. I always get those streets mixed.

SENDEMUP (*jumping into the fray*). Mr. Mortimer, is it not true that on several occasions you have pub-licly expressed your contempt for the traffic regulations of our town?

MATT (*bitterly*). I can't help it, sir. These one-way streets are enough to drive a man crazy. I have to start to work an hour earlier to get there on time and go miles out of my way. Every six weeks they shuffle the signs, and I have to learn a new route. And the parking! I start to a movie matinee, and I'm lucky to be in my seat for the first evening show. I drive for hours to find a parking place.

(*The jury and spectators applaud.*)

SENDEMUP (*sarcastically*). I understand. It is our traffic laws and not your pig-headedness that is to blame. You don't like our traffic laws, so you don't obey them.

MATT (*desperately*). I didn't say I don't obey 'em. I said I don't like 'em, and I don't.

(*Everyone but* SENDEMUP *applauds as* MATT *stalks to his seat.*)

SENDEMUP (*to* CLERK). Call Miss Violet Vale.

CLERK. Miss Violet Vale, take the stand, please. (VIOLET *sits in the witness chair.*) Raise your right hand, please. (*She shakes her head and smiles pathetically. Her right arm was injured and she can't raise it. Everyone feels sorry.*) Er—I mean—raise your left hand. (*She does.*) Do you blah-blah-blah-blah?

VIOLET (*touching the book*). I do.

SENDEMUP. Now, don't be nervous, Miss Vale.

VIOLET. No, Mr. Sendemup.

SENDEMUP. Miss Vale, is it not true that as a result of your injuries received in the accident on October twentieth your right arm has become permanently stiff and you are unable to use it?

VIOLET. Yes, sir. I'm unable to use my right arm. My doctor said I could, but you said I couldn't.

JUDGE (*as* VIOLET *is turned away from the jury*). Speak to the jury, Miss Vale.

VIOLET. Yes, your Honor. (*Turns to jury.*) Good afternoon.

JURY (*in concert, rising and bowing as one man*). Good afternoon, Miss Vale.

SENDEMUP. Miss Vale, where did the car hit you?

VIOLET. My doctor says at the junction of the dorsal and the cervical vertebrae.

SMITH (*sotto voce to* MARTIN). Man and boy, I've

lived in these parts fifty years, and I never even heard of that place.

MARTIN (*sotto voce*). It's her collarbone, I think.

SMITH. Then why in thunder didn't she say so?

GETEMOFF (*as there is a pause*). Miss Vale, if you were so badly injured, why did you wait so long to take legal action against my client?

VIOLET. It took him (*pointing to* SENDEMUP) a long time to find out if he (*pointing to* MATT) was worth enough to be sued.

(*Everybody laughs but the* JUDGE *and* SENDEMUP.)

GETEMOFF. Miss Vale, didn't you see the officer under the traffic light on George Street motioning to you?

VIOLET. Oh, yes, but I couldn't tell by the way he wiggled his thumb whether he wanted me to stop, or go on, or if he was just waving at me. He's awfully good-looking in his uniform.

GETEMOFF (*sympathetically*). Which arm was hurt, Miss Vale?

VIOLET. My left. (SENDEMUP *clears his throat.*) Er—I mean my right one. I never can tell them apart.

GETEMOFF. And you are, as a consequence of this accident, unable to raise your right arm more than a few inches.

VIOLET. Yes, sir.

SENDEMUP (*to* JUDGE). Your Honor, I protest. He took my witness right away from me. I object.

JUDGE. Objection overruled, and I wish somebody'd take *you* away. Sit down and be still. I'm beginning to enjoy this.

GETEMOFF. Thank you, your Honor. Now, Miss Vale, would you mind showing the jury just how far you can raise your right arm since it was injured in the accident? (*With very great effort,* VIOLET *raises her right arm a few inches; then lets it drop into her lap with a sigh of relief. Audience sighs, too.*) Thank you very much, Miss Vale. You have my deepest sympathy. How high could you raise it before the accident? (*Without thinking,* VIOLET *quickly raises her right arm high above her head, then drops it quickly as she realizes what she has done.* GETEMOFF *sits, smiling.* VIOLET *is too overcome to move.*)

VIOLET. O-oh!

SENDEMUP (*rising quickly*). The witness made a mistake. You all heard her say she never could tell her arms apart. It was her left arm that was injured.

VIOLET (*hurriedly*). Yes. I can't lift that at all. See? (*Tries vainly to lift the left arm.*)

SENDEMUP. That's all, Miss Vale. (*She returns to her seat and covers her face with both hands.*)

JUDGE. There's something fishy about this whole case. Everybody's lying like blazes. Jury, I wish we had the power to send 'em all up for twenty years. Do your darnedest, anyway. Retire and cough up a verdict.

FOREMAN. We have one now, your Honor.

JUDGE. Good. Violet Vale, stand up and get what's coming to you.

SENDEMUP (*indignantly*). Your Honor, my client is not the prisoner.

JUDGE. All right, all right. (*To* MATT.) You stand up, then. (MATT *stands.*) What is your verdict, jury?

FOREMAN. We, the jury, find the defendant, Matt Mortimer, not guilty, but (*to* MATT) don't do it again.

MATT. Thank you very much.

JUDGE. Court is adjourned. (*Goes off right as all stand.*)

VIOLET (*to* MATT). I'm sorry, Mr. Mortimer.

SENDEMUP. I'll appeal the case, Miss Vale.

VIOLET. Oh, I couldn't do that. (*Coyly.*) I think Matt's cute.

(SENDEMUP *stalks off at right, followed by* GETEMOFF, *laughing.*)

MATT. Er—could I drive you home, Violet?

VIOLET. Yes, Matt.

(MATT *and* VIOLET *go off at left.* EMMA *and* LUCY *glare after them.*)

EMMA. They might have taken us, too. After all we did for her!

LUCY. You did. I never got to answer a single question.

(EMMA *and* LUCY *go off at left, followed by* BROWN, JONES, SMITH, *and* MARTIN.)

MARTIN (*as they go*). Funny way to end a trial.

SMITH. Funny trial.

JONES *and* BROWN. Stupid! (*The four men exeunt at left.*)

(BLAKE *and* DRAKE *start off at left.*)

DRAKE (*as they go*). Well, we got Matt outa that mess. Didn't we?

BLAKE. Yep. So he turns around and gets himself into another.

(*The room is now empty except for the* CLERK. *He sits and takes the comic book out of his pocket.*)

CLERK (*scornfully*). People! They're worse than traffic!

CURTAIN

BODY, BODY, WHO'S GOT THE BODY?

(*A detective farce*)

FOR ELEVEN MEN

CHARACTERS

PINKERTON HAWKSHAW, *a correspondence school detective*

MRS. MARCELLA CUNNINGHAM MITFORD, *the domineering wife*

RONALD MITFORD (RONNIE), *her henpecked husband*

CHARLES CLARKE (CHUCK), *the butler*

MORLEY MICHAEL MCBRIDE, *the cook*

JERRY JONES, *Pinkerton's secretary*

ROGER CUNNINGHAM, *Marcella's uncle*

SHERLOCK MASON, *Pinkerton's assistant*

HERBERT DAVIS, *an encyclopedia salesman*

BILL BENSON, *the paper boy*

MIKE MORAN, *Ronald's pal*

TIME—*Late one afternoon the week before Easter.*

PLACE—*Living room of the Mitford home.*

COSTUMES AND CHARACTERISTICS.—Pinkerton is not very smart but means well. He wears an enormous badge. Marcella, a part to be played by a man, is a woman of uncertain age, gushing manner, and a fixed habit of having her own way. She talks all the time and is dramatic and over-dressed. Ronald is usually meek and long-suffering. Chuck is a tough guy but puts up a dignified bluff for Marcella. Morley is pale and anaemic, talks little, and shrugs frequently. Jerry is not so dumb, very literal, and disgusted with everything.

Uncle Roger is pompous and conceited, but he under-
stands Marcella. Sherlock is a rough and somewhat
sinister chap. Davis is a bustling go-getter. Bill is
sixteen and revels in excitement. Mike is shabby but is
evidently good company. All the men wear everyday
attire.

PROPERTIES.—For Pinkerton: suitcase filled with disguises, such as beards and spectacles, book of hints for
sleuths, and a sign reading, "Danger, Pinkerton Hawkshaw working"; bottle of aspirin tablets. For Jerry:
huge notebook and pencil. For Davis: brief case containing book samples. For Bill: armful of newspapers.
For Ronnie and Mike: a suitcase apiece.

SCENE: *The well-furnished living room of the Mitford home. It has two doors: one at right leading to
the kitchen and the other at left leading to the front
hall and upstairs. Up left is a small desk, on which
are papers, books, etc. In the desk drawer is a small
pistol. Back of the desk is a chair. Up right is a small
table, on which are a telephone and a large paperweight.
On the rug near the table are a broken fingernail and a
drop of blood. Several chairs may be added to dress
the stage.*

At the rise of the curtain, the stage is empty, but
MARCELLA *enters at once at left and looks around on
the floor at the rear as if expecting to see something.
Alarmed at not seeing it, she grows excited, looks under
the desk, lifts a corner of the rug, then goes to the
telephone and takes down the receiver.*

MARCELLA (*speaking into transmitter*). Charter
7, 7, 11, 11, 13, 13, and hurry, please. This is an
emergency. (*Bites her nails.*) Is this Charter 7, 7,
11, 11, 13, 13? Are you sure? May I speak to Pinker-

ton Hawkshaw, the private eye—I mean the private detective? (*Pauses.*) Yes, I'll wait. (*Bites her nails and taps her foot.*) Hello. Pinkerton Hawkshaw? This is Mrs. Ronald Mitford of 119 Lee Avenue. Come here immediately if not sooner. I've just shot my husband. (*Pause.*) No. I don't want the police. I want a detective. (*Pauses.*) What for? Why, to find the body. It's disappeared. Come and find it. I'm expecting company and I can't have a stray body lying around loose. Don't ring the bell. Come right in at the front door. I'll do my nails while I'm waiting for you.

She hangs up, searches the room again, shrugs her shoulders, and goes off at left. CHUCK *and* MORLEY *enter at right, for no apparent reason, but the show must go on.*

CHUCK. I'm gonna leave this dump, Morley. I won't be the Mitford butler any longer. I can't stand the missus. She keeps forgettin' I can leave any time. She bosses me just as if I was her old man.

MORLEY. Lousy with importance.

CHUCK. Just lousy, period. How can you cook for a dame like that, McBride?

MORLEY (*shrugging*). All alike.

CHUCK. Yeah, only some's worse'n others. I'd like to send her a time bomb for Easter. (*Loud footsteps are heard off left.*) Sh-h!

MORLEY. What's that?

CHUCK. I don't know. I'll listen again. (*Footsteps come nearer.*)

MORLEY. Company. Let's scram. (*They rush off at right.*)

PINKERTON, JERRY, *and* SHERLOCK *enter at left.*

PINKERTON *carries the sign,* "Danger. *Pinkerton Hawk-shaw working," which he places on the floor in front of the desk, and a suitcase, which he sets down beside the desk. He takes from his pocket a huge bottle labeled "aspirin," swallows a few pills, and places the bottle on the desk.*

PINKERTON. Jerry and Sherlock, just sit down while I get ready to work. Jerry, you'll take down everything everybody says.

JERRY. You're the only one that's saying anything, boss.

PINKERTON. I mean when I call witnesses.

JERRY. Aren't you going to look for the body?

PINKERTON. All in good time, my boy; all in good time.

SHERLOCK (*to* JERRY). Maybe he'll find it at that. Luck is what some folks use instead of brains.

PINKERTON. You both can help me. Two heads are better than none.

(JERRY *sits.* SHERLOCK *looks at the books on the desk up left.* PINKERTON *just gazes around.*)

SHERLOCK. Somebody here sure likes murder stories. "The Corpse in the Coffee Pot." No wonder she conked her old man. Prepare for the worst, Jerry.

JERRY. I always do, but when it comes it's worse than I expected.

PINKERTON. Now, now, boys. Just a little murder. Sherlock, I shall use a different disguise for each witness.

SHERLOCK. But why?

PINKERTON. It confuses them.

JERRY. It confuses me, too.

PINKERTON (*opening suitcase, taking out his book,*

and putting it on desk). Now, to work. (*Takes the
gun from the desk drawer.*)   Aha, the gun!
  JERRY. Fingerprints?
  PINKERTON. Of course not. Fingerprints are old-
fashioned. I use psychology.
  SHERLOCK. Pinkerton, you're crazy.
  PINKERTON (*blandly*). My boy, I may be a fool, but
I'm an intelligent fool. I'll solve this case in twenty
minutes. (*Picks up a piece of nail from the rug.*)
Here, by the telephone, is a large slice of fingernail.
Somebody was nervous. Who? Mrs. Mitford. Here
on the rug is a bloodstain. Whose? Mr. Mitford's.
Now all we have to do is find the body.
  SHERLOCK. Body, body, who's got the body?

  MARCELLA *enters at left.*

  MARCELLA. Good afternoon, gentlemen.

  (JERRY *rises politely, then sits and begins to take
notes.*)

  PINKERTON. Mrs. Mitford, I—
  MARCELLA (*sitting*). You want to hear all about it.
Sit down and I'll tell you. (PINKERTON *and* SHERLOCK
sit.) I'm so upset I'll enjoy talking to someone. After
all, murdering one's husband is sort of wearing, especially when the body disappears. Poor dear Ronnie!
It seems like only yesterday, or perhaps even tomorrow,
when I first met him. Eighteen months we've been
married. I've given him the best years of my life. I
did my best to get along with poor dear Ronnie. I left
no stone unturned. The trouble with turning stones is
what comes out from under them. Right?
  THE THREE MEN (*in concert*). Dead right. (PINK-

ERTON *takes aspirin pills*.)

MARCELLA. All Ronnie cared about was meals. Home was just a filling station to him. I have a fine cook and a good butler. I prefer men servants. Ronnie didn't. That's why I did. But every Thursday, on the cook's night out, I get dinner. All frozen food, it's true, but I thaw it myself.

PINKERTON. And this afternoon, Mrs. Mitford?

MARCELLA. Oh, yes, this afternoon. Today is my birthday. I'm having a dinner party tonight—all the best people in town. I was so happy this morning; but every silver lining has a cloud. Ronnie began to be cruel right after breakfast. He wanted me to ask an old school friend of his tonight, and I couldn't change my plans. I just couldn't. He insisted.

PINKERTON. So you shot him.

MARCELLA. Yes. After lunch we were alone in here, and he begged me to let him bring that friend home. And then he said he'd bring him anyway. Everything went lavender before my eyes—

PINKERTON (*interrupts*). You mean black, don't you, Mrs. Mitford?

MARCELLA. Dear me, no! Black is terribly unbecoming to me. Lavender. And I shot him.

PINKERTON. Where?

MARCELLA (*puzzled*). Where? Why, right here.

PINKERTON. No, no. Where did the shot hit him?

MARCELLA. I didn't look. I just fired and he fell. Blood came from his head. I can't stand the sight of blood. I ran upstairs. I was nervous, and I just took a little nap to pull myself together. Then when I waked up and came down, there wasn't any body. You must find it before the guests come to dinner.

PINKERTON. But the police—

MARCELLA (*carelessly*). I'll tell the police tomorrow

when the party is over and you've found Ronnie. The judge will understand. His wife and I belong to the same bridge club.

PINKERTON (*taking more aspirin*). How many people in the house?

SHERLOCK. I checked on that while you were packing your disguises. Charles Clarke, the butler, commonly called Chuck, Morley Michael McBride, the cook, and Mr. Roger Cunningham, Mrs. Mitford's uncle. Right?

MARCELLA. Dead right. Er—I mean yes—correct.

PINKERTON. Mrs. Mitford, you go upstairs and take another little nap while I question these men. I see you like murder stories. Is your husband a bookworm, too?

MARCELLA. No, just an ordinary one.

PINKERTON. Did you get the idea of shooting your husband from these books?

MARCELLA. Well, yes—and no. Most of the murders you read about are so cruel. I often wanted to push Ronnie downstairs, but he always made me go in front of him. I thought of throwing that paperweight at him, but I might have broken the window.

SHERLOCK. Poison?

MARCELLA (*shocked*). Oh, no! Poison is so unethical. The victim has no warning. Not that Ronnie was ethical. When I think of the way he's broken my heart and wrecked my whole life, and now he's spoiled my dinner party—and on my birthday, too! (*Exits at left.*)

SHERLOCK. That dame has static in her attic.

PINKERTON (*putting on a disguise*). Bring in the cook, Sherlock.

SHERLOCK. O.K., boss. (*Goes off at right.*)

JERRY. I still think we ought to be looking for the body.

PINKERTON. My boy, remember truth is like toothpaste. The only way to get it out is to apply pressure around the edges.

SHERLOCK *reënters at right with* MORLEY.

PINKERTON. You are Morley Michael McBride, cook. Do you like it here?

MORLEY (*shrugging*). So-so.

PINKERTON. What kind of man is—was—Mr. Mitford?

MORLEY. Meek.

PINKERTON. Do you like Mrs. Mitford?

MORLEY. Nope. Don't like any women.

PINKERTON. What would you say if I told you Mrs. Mitford had shot Mr. Mitford?

MORLEY (*shrugging*). Nothing.

PINKERTON. You're not much help.

MORLEY. Nope.

PINKERTON. Go back to the kitchen, but don't leave the house. (MORLEY *shrugs and exits at right.* PINKERTON *takes aspirin.*) What do you make of him, Jerry?

JERRY. Nothing.

PINKERTON. You and me both. Sherlock, get the butler. (*Changes his disguise while waiting for the butler.*)

Reënter SHERLOCK *at right, followed by* CHUCK.

PINKERTON. Your name and position here?

CHUCK. Charles Clarke, butler.

PINKERTON. You like it here?

CHUCK. He's O.K. She's a mess. A heart of gold encased in a lump of concrete. Sweet—too darned sweet. Two lumps of her in a cup of coffee, and you couldn't drink it.

PINKERTON. Clarke, did you know that Mrs. Mitford killed her husband this afternoon—shot him right here in this room?

CHUCK (*calmly*). Could be. I always say it's a small world but a nasty one. Maybe she didn't like the birthday present he brought her, or maybe he didn't bring one.

PINKERTON (*thinking deeply*). So you're the butler. Clarke, you're the suspect number one!

CHUCK (*annoyed*). Say that again, and you'll be the corpse number two. By the way, if the boss is murdered, where's the body?

PINKERTON. Don't you know? It's disappeared.

CHUCK (*startled*). You mean there ain't no corpus delicious?

PINKERTON. There ain't.

CHUCK. Ask that uncle of hers. He never misses anything. I think he's got a universal joint in his neck. I don't trust anybody in this house, includin' you.

PINKERTON. Go back to the kitchen and wait, Clarke. I'll want to see you later. (*Exit* CHUCK *at right.* PINKERTON *swallows more pills and reads from his book.*) "Coax witnesses. Be calm. Frighten them. Be jolly. Appear to believe. Act doubtful. Use big words. Speak simply." (*Shuts the book.*) Wonder what I'd better try next. (*Reads from the book again.*) "Never hesitate." (*Slams the book down.*) Right, dead right! I'll just take the bull by the horns and throw it. (*Changes his disguise again.*) Sherlock, bring in Mr. Cunningham.

SHERLOCK *goes off at left.* JERRY *looks at* PINKERTON *and shakes his head despairingly.* UNCLE ROGER *enters at right.*

UNCLE ROGER. What's the big idea?

PINKERTON (*sternly*). Sit down. Your niece shot and killed her husband this afternoon. The body has disappeared.

UNCLE ROGER. Do you know what you're talking about? I'm sure I don't.

PINKERTON. What kind of man was Mr. Mitford?

UNCLE ROGER. A gentleman, naturally. Quiet, refined, but inhibited. He completely lacked self-assertion. He continually effaced himself from any scene of conflict.

PINKERTON (*dazed*). Er—what did he say, Jerry?

JERRY (*reading from notes*). Mr. Mitford wasn't a man. He was a mouse—a nice mouse, but—a mouse.

PINKERTON. Oh! Then, Mr. Cunningham, you do not think he would have given his wife reason to murder him?

UNCLE ROGER. There is never any reason in anything Marcella does. I have always thought her mother, my poor sister Mary, should have thrown away the baby and kept the stork. Marcella has delusions of grandeur.

PINKERTON (*stuck again*). What's that, Jerry?

JERRY (*reading from notes*). She thinks she's a big shot.

PINKERTON. Oh!

UNCLE ROGER. Marcella makes everybody's life miserable. Now I love work. I can sit and watch folks do it for hours. Ronnie worked like a dog—and got treated like one. Now if Ronnie had shot her, I could understand that. After all, it's a long worm that has no turning.

PINKERTON. Mr. Cunningham, have you any idea where the body is hidden?

UNCLE ROGER. Where have you looked?

PINKERTON. Nowhere, yet. If he's dead, he can't get away.

UNCLE ROGER. If I knew where the body is, I wouldn't tell. Let the unfortunate man enjoy himself for a few minutes.

PINKERTON (*taking aspirin*). Mr. Cunningham, give me your honest opinion. Do you think your niece killed her husband?

UNCLE ROGER. By that remark, I suppose you are implying that Marcella used wishful thinking to such an alarming extent that she actually thinks she did kill him. That is an uncommon state of affairs, but Marcella is an uncommon female. She reads all the murder stories published, and that tends to brutalize her nature. She takes a great many extension courses in psychology in Columbia, and you know what Columbia does to an unbalanced mind—or you wouldn't, would you? Or would you? Marcella's excessive sweetness and apparent helplessness may be the outward signs of her inward quality. Or they may be just a smoke screen to hide her real self. That, sir, is my answer to your question. (*Exit at right.*)

PINKERTON (*weakly*). Read it back, Jerry.

JERRY (*reading from notes*). Question: Do you think your niece killed her husband? Answer: Maybe.

PINKERTON. That's what I thought he said, "Maybe."

SHERLOCK *enters at left, leading* BILL *with his armful of papers.*

SHERLOCK. This is Bill, the paper boy. I thought he might know something.

BILL (*scared*). Honest, I didn't do it—whatever it is.

PINKERTON. Sit down, son. (*Changes his disguise.*)

BILL (*thrilled*). Oh—a magician!

PINKERTON. Just a detective. Tell me your name.

BILL. Bill Benson. I deliver the (*name of the town paper*) to Mrs. Mitford every day. Would you like me to bring it to you, sir?

PINKERTON. No, thank you, Bill. Listen, my boy. This afternoon Mrs. Mitford shot and killed her husband. Now the body has disappeared.

BILL. I didn't take it! Honest, I didn't!

PINKERTON. You haven't seen the body?

BILL. Gosh, no. Where is it?

PINKERTON. That's what I'm trying to find out.

Doorbell rings loudly off left. All jump. SHERLOCK *goes off at left and returns with* DAVIS *who carries a brief case containing samples of the book he is selling.*

SHERLOCK. This guy was ringing the doorbell.

PINKERTON. Who are you?

DAVIS. Herbert Davis. And who are you?

SHERLOCK. This is the very famous detective, Pinkerton Hawkshaw.

DAVIS. Hi ya, Lockshaw.

PINKERTON. Hawkshaw.

DAVIS. I want to see Mrs. Mitford. I'm selling the Universal Encyclopedia, and she's thinking of buying one. Where is she?

PINKERTON. What do you know about Mrs. Mitford?

DAVIS. Well, we're not having an affair, if that's what you mean. She's not my type. She doesn't cooperate with her clothes. I thought she was interested in the pages on murder in my book.

PINKERTON. What do you know about Mr. Mitford?

DAVIS. Not a thing, Mr. Bockshaw.

PINKERTON (*patiently*). Hawkshaw. This afternoon Mrs. Mitford shot her husband.

DAVIS (*interested*). What do you know! My wife always says it takes a mighty good husband to be better than none. Maybe Mrs. Mitford thought so, too. Say, Mr. Mockraw—

PINKERTON. Hawkshaw—

DAVIS. I think the dame's wacky.

PINKERTON. Could be. She shot her husband, and the body disappeared.

DAVIS. Mr. Handsaw—

PINKERTON. Hawkshaw. I know what you're about to say, and I *don't* want your encyclopedia, no matter how many pages it has on the art of being a detective. Just sit over there next to Bill. (DAVIS *sits*.) Jerry, what have we learned from the witnesses?

JERRY (*reading from notes*). Mrs. Mitford talked a lot and said nothing. McBride, the cook, said nothing and didn't talk. Clarke, the butler—tough guy, doesn't like Mrs. Mitford. Roger Cunningham says Mrs. Mitford thinks she's a big shot. (*Looks up from notes.*) I don't think she is. Anyway, many a big shot turns out to be only a blank cartridge.

PINKERTON (*excitedly*). Wait! Hold everything! (*Takes a handful of aspirin.*)

JERRY and SHERLOCK (*in concert*). What's the matter, boss?

PINKERTON. I've got an idea, and I must tie a knot in its tail so it can't get away. Sherlock, bring in everybody. (*Calls off left.*) Mrs. Mitford, come down, please.

(SHERLOCK *goes off right, and* PINKERTON *changes his disguise.*)

DAVIS. Now I've seen everything.

BILL. It's better than the movies.

SHERLOCK *reënters at right with* CHUCK, MCBRIDE, *and* UNCLE ROGER *just as* MARCELLA *enters at left.*

PINKERTON. Be seated, please.

(*All the newcomers sit.*)

BILL. Now it's a minstrel show.

UNCLE ROGER (*sneeringly*). Well, my good sleuth, have you got away to a flying stop?

CHUCK. He hasn't even looked for the body. I don't think he's much of a detective.

PINKERTON (*coldly*). Have you ever qualified as a sleuth, Charles Clarke?

CHUCK. Chuck to you. And you don't have to be able to lay a good egg to know a bad one when you smell it.

MARCELLA (*shocked*). Don't be vulgar, Clarke.

CHUCK (*the perfect butler*). I beg your pardon, madam.

BILL. Gosh!

MARCELLA. It's almost time for the dinner party. Have you found poor dear Ronnie? Where have you looked?

PINKERTON. I haven't looked anywhere. I've got a bird in hand and to heck with the flocks in the bushes. Nobody leaves this room till the—er—body is found.

UNCLE ROGER. Do you expect it to come walking in?

MARCELLA. Don't talk like that, Uncle Roger. It sounds so heartless.

SHERLOCK (*to* PINKERTON). Boss, we seem to be at a standstill.

PINKERTON (*calmly*). Worse places to be at.

UNCLE ROGER. Call the police.

MARCELLA. No, Uncle Roger. I can't have my party spoiled.

CHUCK. I won't believe Mr. Mitford's dead till he tells me so himself.

(*Voices are heard off left. All except* PINKERTON *are startled. He just smiles and removes his disguise.*)

RONNIE (*off left*). Well, here we are, Mike, and don't be scared. I won't let her hurt you.

MIKE (*off left*). Don't worry about me. Look out for yourself.

RONNIE MITFORD *and* MIKE *enter at left.* RONNIE *looks around in surprise.*

RONNIE (*to* MARCELLA). Are these your dinner guests?

MARCELLA (*shrieking*). Ronnie, it's you! It's you!

PINKERTON (*smugly*). The body comes walking in— as I thought.

MARCELLA. But—

PINKERTON (*interrupts*). Mr. Mitford, your loving wife thought she had killed you. She was quite annoyed when your body disappeared. It interfered with the party.

RONNIE (*amused*). Too bad.

PINKERTON. Sit down and tell us all about it. Won't you?

BILL. Just like "Mr. Keen, the Tracer of Lost Persons."

RONNIE. First let me introduce my good friend, Mike Moran, to you all.

MIKE (*politely*). Charmed, I'm sure.

MARCELLA. The one you wanted to ask to dinner?

RONNIE. The one I did ask to dinner—but not here.

PINKERTON. It isn't time for dinner yet. Tell us about the shooting.

RONNIE (*as he and* MIKE *sit*). Gladly. My wife has read so many murder stories she's filled with ideas. And she doesn't approve of me. Now I know I can live only once, but I'd like to make my once last as long as possible. So I've been taking precautions.

PINKERTON (*smiling*). Blank cartridges in the gun.

RONNIE. Exactly.

JERRY and SHERLOCK (*in concert*). Blanks!

MARCELLA (*to* RONNIE, *furiously*). Why—you—you contemptible sneak! How—how—unkind! How unethical!

SHERLOCK. Yeah, wasn't it?

RONNIE. I had determined if and when she shot me, to make believe I was dead, just to see how she'd act— like Lady Macbeth or Lizzie Borden. So, when she fired, I fell, but when I fell my head hit the corner of the table, and I cut myself. I went out like a light.

PINKERTON. So that's where the blood came from.

RONNIE. When I came to, I was alone, so I just hurried out to meet Mike.

MARCELLA (*bitterly*). Leaving me alone to suffer. And I hired this—this detective to find your body. I won't pay him—not one cent. Ronnie, you've completely ruined my birthday.

MIKE (*to* RONNIE). With her for a friend, you don't need any enemies. Do you?

UNCLE ROGER. Ronnie, you poor dope, why did you come back?

RONNIE. Mike wanted to meet Marcella, and I wanted to get my clothes.

CHUCK. Where you goin', boss?

RONNIE. Mike and I are going to work on a new kind of atomic bomb, the most deadly and dangerous thing you can imagine. At last I shall have a quiet, peaceful life. (*To* MARCELLA.) Well, happy birth day, Marcella.

CHUCK and MORLEY (*in concert*). Could you get us jobs like that, too, boss?

MIKE. It's a hard life, boys.

CHUCK. You've never worked for Mrs. Mitford. You ain't seen nothin' yet.

MARCELLA. But my dinner party! (*Sobs bitterly.*)

PINKERTON. You may all go, gentlemen. (*Puts his book and disguises in the suitcase.*) I'll send you my bill tomorrow, Mrs. Mitford.

SHERLOCK (*to* JERRY). I always said Pinkerton was smart—in a stupid sort of way.

(RONNIE *and* MIKE *exeunt at left.* MORLEY *and* CHUCK *go off at right, followed by* DAVIS *and* BILL.)

MARCELLA. What have I ever done that such things should happen to me and on my birthday, too! I'll have my party just the same. I'll call up the hotel and have a dinner sent over—and waiters— Oh, dear! Where can I get waiters? (*Weeps.*)

(RONNIE *and* MIKE *reënter at left, each carrying a suitcase, just as* MORLEY *and* CHUCK *run on at right.*)

CHUCK. Somebody's stole all the silver. It was on the table in the dining room, and there ain't a piece left!

MARCELLA (*jumping up*). What? My silver gone?

(MORLEY *shrugs assent, and* CHUCK *smiles happily.*)

CHUCK. Right, dead right!

MARCELLA. And a detective in the house!

PINKERTON (*picking up his sign*). Madam, you hired me to find a body, not to guard the silver.

RONNIE. There goes your dinner party, my dear Marcella.

MARCELLA. Oh, this is too much! (*Faints in her chair.*)

(*All the others start for the left door except* UNCLE ROGER, *who stands at right.*)

PINKERTON (*at the left door*). Come on, boys. Happy birthday, Mrs. Mitford.

JERRY and SHERLOCK (*in concert*). Happy birthday, Mrs. Mitford. (*They follow* PINKERTON *off at left.*)

UNCLE ROGER (*realizing he is left alone with his niece, starts for the left door*). Hey, wait for baby! (*Forgetting his dignity, he rushes off at left.*)

(MARCELLA *rises, gazes around in rage and dismay, and goes down to the center front.*)

MARCELLA (*bitterly, but with resignation*). Oh, well, maybe it's a good thing I didn't kill him. Murder is so hard to explain! Poor dear Ronnie! He's really such a nice person; but nice persons do the damnedest things!

(*She goes to the desk, picks up the bottle* PINKERTON *forgot, shakes out a handful of aspirin tablets, and gulps them down as—*)

THE CURTAIN FALLS

THE NUMBERS GAME
(*A radio travesty*)
FOR FIVE MEN, FIVE WOMEN, AND EXTRAS

CHARACTERS

ANNOUNCER

DR. SOCRATES WEBSTER (M. C.), *Master of Ceremonies*

MISS MARY JANE JENNINGS, *a rather stolid young woman*

MR. ARCHIBALD ROSS, *an ordinary chap who tries hard*

MRS. SARAH SHARP, *a gay old lady*

MR. SAMUEL SHARP, *a gay old gentleman*

MISS IRMA INSLEY, *a pretty nurse*

MR. GEORGE GRANT, *an embarrassed teen-ager*

MISS LORENA MILLS, *a peppy dame who loves to talk*

MRS. VIOLA BURTON, *a nervous housewife*

MEMBERS OF THE STUDIO AUDIENCE—*any number*

TIME—*Any evening.*

PLACE—*Studio 13 in Station OOO.*

COSTUMES AND CHARACTERISTICS.—The announcer is a genial chap who enunciates with painful distinctness. Dr. Webster is a pompous, too-genial chap, with all the worst characteristics of a master of ceremonies or a quiz director. All the characters wear street attire.

SCENE: *The studio of a radio station. There are two entrances at left and right respectively. The backdrop consists of dark curtains or screens. Just in front of it are rows of chairs facing the audience, in which sit the studio audience and the contestants. A little*

*down right are the chair and small desk of the M. C.,
with his microphone standing beside the desk, which is
covered with papers. A little down left is the Announcer's chair, with a second microphone standing
beside it. At center back, fastened high up on the dark
curtains or the screen, is a large chart upon which the
subjects are listed so that they are clearly seen: literature, music, movies, geography, sports, politics, inventions, history, science, and cooking. Down center near
the footlights is a third microphone, which is used by
the contestants.*

*At the rise of the curtain, the studio audience and
contestants are in their seats up center. Immediately
the Announcer enters at left just as the M. C. enters
at right. They go to their respective chairs and sit.*

ANNOUNCER (*rising*). Good evening, ladies and gentlemen. Welcome to Station OOO and the Numbers
Game. This evening's amusement with its remarkable
prizes is made possible to you by our sponsor, the United
Benevolent Order of Junk Dealers, Inc. How about a
hand for the junk dealers? (*Audience applauds.*) Here
is our Master of Ceremonies, Dr. Socrates Webster, who
knows all the questions. (*Applause.*) We hope you'll
know all the answers. It pays to be smart when you
play the numbers game.

M. C. (*rising*). Good evening, ladies and gentlemen
of the radio audience, and our friends in the studio.
Now, before we begin, may I explain our procedure?
As if you didn't know, you smart people! Each contestant—your names have already been picked from a
hat by the announcer, Mr. Ken Ross (*applause*)—will
choose a subject from those listed on the wall. He will
also choose a number. I shall ask the question bearing

that number. If the contestant wins he gets a wonderful prize. If he doesn't—oh, well, let's not think
about that. But, win or lose, every contestant gets a
chance at the sixty-nine-dollar question and the reward
for answering that is so great I can't even remember
what it is. All ready, Ken.

ANNOUNCER (*takes a paper from his pocket and
looks at it*). The first contestant is Miss Mary Jane
Jennings of Pensacola, Florida.

(MISS JENNINGS *comes down to front.*)

M. C.   Hello, Miss Jennings. We're very glad to
have you with us tonight. And how is everything in
Florida?

MISS JENNINGS (*flatly*). All right.

M. C.   That's fine, just fine! What subject do you
wish to take?

MISS JENNINGS.   Geography.

M. C.   Fine! What number?

MISS JENNINGS.   Twenty-six.

M. C. (*looking at the questions on the desk*). Geography, twenty-six. Here we are. Now, Miss Jennings,
if you answer this question correctly you will receive a
Great Dane dog named Dulcimer, a five years' supply
of dog biscuit—

GUESTS (*in concert*). A-ah!

M. C. (*continuing*). Also a diamond studded collar,
for the dog, not you, Miss Jennings, and a nylon leash
with a ruby clasp.

GUESTS.   A-ah!

M. C.   And now the question. Miss Jennings: What
city in the U. S. A. bears the name of a state, of our
first president, and is also our national capital?

MISS JENNINGS.   Er—er—

M. C. Hurry, Miss Jennings. Think of the Great Dane—I mean the city. You'll have no trouble washing the dog, though he weighs almost a ton.

Miss Jennings. Er—er—

(Announcer *rings bell attached to his microphone.*)

M. C. Two seconds more, Miss Jennings.

Miss Jennings. I know—Washington.

(*The guests applaud.*)

M. C. Fine, just fine, Miss Jennings! Your winnings will be delivered to you tomorrow. Stick around for the sixty-nine-dollar question.

(Miss Jennings *returns to her seat, still unexcited.*)

Announcer. The next contestant is Mr. Archibald Ross, of Brooklyn, N. Y.

(*The guests applaud frantically.* Ross *comes down to front.*)

M. C. Glad to see you, Mr. Ross. Just what do you do in Brooklyn?

Mr. Ross. I'm a plumber, doctor.

M. C. Fine, just fine, Mr. Ross! On a vacation?

Mr. Ross. Yeah—I mean yes, doctor.

M. C. And what subject do you choose, sir?

Mr. Ross. Sports, question 1.

M. C. You can see Mr. Ross is a businessman. He wastes no time. No indeed. That's fine! Now, Mr. Ross, think carefully. If you answer this question correctly you will receive a complete set of the Encyclopedia

Britannica, bound in purple velvet, a solid gold vanity case, and a book of three-cent stamps. Now, tell in which branch of sports each of these men distinguished himself: Babe Ruth, Joe Louis, Izaak Walton.

MR. ROSS. Babe Ruth, baseball; Joe Louis, fighter. Er—er—who was that last guy?

M. C. Izaak Walton.

MR. ROSS. He was the jockey who won the Kentucky Derby last year.

M. C. Oh, I'm so sorry, Mr. Ross. Think! It's a whale of a question I know, but there's nothing fishy about it.

MR. ROSS. Was he the man who won the—? Er—I don't know.

M. C. Audience?

GUESTS (*in concert*). Fishing.

MR. ROSS. I protest. Fishing ain't a sport. Even the worms don't get any exercise when a man goes fishing.

(*The guests applaud.*)

M. C. Mr. Ross, because you did so well we shall give you the prize anyway. Stick around for the big event.

(MR. ROSS *resumes his seat.*)

ANNOUNCER (*consulting his list*). The next contestant is Mrs. Sarah Sharp, from Philadelphia.

M. C. (*as* MRS. SHARP *comes down to the microphone*). Hello, Mrs. Sharp. How are you tonight?

MRS. SHARP. Fine, thank you, Dr. Webster.

M. C. That's just fine, Mrs. Sharp. Is your husband with you?

MRS. SHARP (*pointing*). He's right back there. (MR. SHARP *waves to her.*)

M. C. Fine! Are you here on a visit?

Mrs. Sharp. We're celebrating our fiftieth wedding anniversary.

(*The guests applaud loudly.*)

M. C. Wonderful! I hope you win a prize tonight. Your husband won his prize fifty years ago. Now, what subject, Mrs. Sharp?

Mrs. Sharp (*looking at the names doubtfully*). I don't know much about any of 'em. Oh, yes—cooking. That's what I'll take.

M. C. Does she feed you well, Mr. Sharp? Do you get fat on good home cooking?

Mr. Sharp. Yes. We eat at a restaurant where they specialize in home cooking.

(*The guests laugh, but* Mrs. Sharp *shakes her head at her husband.*)

M. C. What number, Mrs. Sharp?

Mrs. Sharp. Fifty.

M. C. Number fifty. Mrs. Sharp, if you answer this question correctly this is the prize you'll get: a motorcycle upholstered in red plush, an Oriental scatter rug, and a fountain pen that will write in the dark. Now listen carefully. If you had company for dinner and burned the beefsteak, what would you do?

Mrs. Sharp (*promptly*). Put sunburn oil on it.

M. C. Fine! Oil is right, Mrs. Sharp. Of course the steak wouldn't be sun-burned but— Audience, shall we count that correct?

Guests (*in concert*). Yes!

M. C. And Mrs. Sharp, because it's your anniversary we'll add a fifty-dollar gold piece to your pile of prizes.

Mrs. Sharp. Thank you very much, Dr. Webster. (*Resumes her seat.*)

Announcer. The next contestant is Miss Irma Insley, of Detroit, Michigan. (*Whistles as she comes front.*)

M. C. Good evening, Miss Insley. (*Gets a good look at her and then he whistles also.*) I can tell without asking how you are. You're fine—just fine!

Miss Insley. Thank you, doctor.

M. C. What are you doing after the show—er—I mean what are you doing in our town?

Miss Insley. Spending my vacation. I'm a nurse.

M. C. I think I've got heart trouble. I'll see you about it later. What subject and number, Irma—er—Miss Insley?

Miss Insley. Movies, number nine.

M. C. (*looks up the question*). Miss Insley, if you answer this correctly—and I just know you will—this is what we shall give you: a spun glass bathing suit, a Ford coupé and sixteen pairs of white kid gloves. Now, lend me your pretty ears. Part one. In the movie (*names a very famous moving picture*) did (*names its star actor*) play the hero or the heroine?

Miss Insley. The hero.

M. C. Fine, just fine! Part two, what is the first name of a movie star named (*names a well-known woman movie star*)?

(Miss Insley *gives the Christian name of the star.*)

M. C. Wonderful! Part three, give the missing word in the title of this picture—"The Treasure of the Sierra ———."

Miss Insley. Madre.

M. C. Miss Insley, you are as smart as you are beautiful. And I hope you win the jackpot prize.

Miss Insley. Thank you, doctor. (*Returns to her seat.*)

Announcer. The next contestant is Mr. George Grant. Syracuse, N. Y., is his home.

M. C. (*disappointed*). Oh! Well, welcome to our program, Mr. Grant. How old are you?

Mr. Grant. Seventeen, sir.

M. C. Choose your subject and number.

Mr. Grant. Er—inventions, number 35.

M. C. Inventions, number 35. Fine! (*Reads the question.*) If you answer this question you will win a gold-headed cane with your initials on it, six pairs of fine lace curtains and a two-years' supply of bubble gum. Ready, Mr. Grant?

Mr. Grant. I—I guess so.

M. C. Who invented the lightning rod?

Mr. Grant. Er—er—Fulton.

M. C. Oh, no, Mr. Grant. Think again. He wrote proverbs—"Poor Richard's Almanac."

Mr. Grant. Er—er—Richard III?

M. C. Oh, dear me, Mr. Grant. He was an American. He lived in Philadelphia.

Mr. Grant. I don't know much about Philadelphia.

M. C. Let me ask you another question, Mr. Grant. What station is this?

Mr. Grant. Er—er—O—K—E.

(*The guests groan.*)

M. C. No, Mr. Grant. I'm sorry. However, you worked so hard we'll give you the lace curtains, anyway. Stick around for the jackpot—the sixty-nine-dollar question. Miracles do happen, you know.

(Mr. Grant *returns to his place.*)

ANNOUNCER. The next contestant is Miss Serena Mills. She—

MISS MILLS (*bounding up*). I'm from Trenton, N. J. I'm here visiting my sister, Mrs. Thomas Gray. I'm very well, thank you, and don't ask how old I am because it's none of your business. I choose literature, number thirteen. I'm not superstitious. What do I get if I know the answer, which I certainly expect to do?

(*The guests applaud.*)

M. C. (*gasping and faint*). Er—er— (*Looks it up.*) Literature, 13. The prize, Miss Mills, is an electric sewing machine with all attachments, a season ticket to the opera, and a hand-painted dinner set of the finest china.

MISS MILLS. I could use the sewing machine, though I have a very good dressmaker. I suppose I can give the other stuff away at Christmas time to somebody I don't like. Come on. Let's get on with it. What do you want me to tell you?

M. C. Miss Mills, name five important books and the author of each (*viciously*), without stopping to think.

MISS MILLS. Oh, I never stop to think. It's automatic with me. Here goes. You count 'em, brother. "Uncle Tom's Cabin," by Harriet Beecher Stowe; the Dictionary, by Noah Webster; Longfellow's Poems, by Longfellow; "Vanity Fair," by Thackeray; "A Tale of Two Cities," by Dickens, and that's what I call a book, if you know what I mean; "Pilgrim's Progress," by John Bunyan; Shakespeare's Plays, by Shakespeare— "The Corpse in the Coal Bin," by John Hooten Howlin—a crime club book, and is it woozy!

M. C. Miss Mills, you have given us more than five already. Thank you. That's—

Miss Mills (*interrupting*). —fine, just fine! I know lots more.

M. C. Some other time, Miss Mills. You win, and I know you'll stick around for the jackpot.

(*She returns to her seat, as the guests applaud.*)

Announcer. We have time for just one more contestant, Miss Nola Barton, of Los Angeles, California.

M. C. Hello, Mrs. Barton. I'm afraid we shall have to hurry. Subject and number, please?

Mrs. Barton. Music, number 11.

M. C. If you can identify these tunes correctly, you will receive a fishing rod with all the gadgets imaginable, a complete set of living room furniture, and two hand-embroidered dish towels. (*Motions to the Announcer who motions off left.*)

(*The music of "Sweet Adeline" is heard, played on a piano or victrola.*)

M. C. Name the tunes as soon as the music stops, Mrs. Barton, please.

Mrs. Barton. "Sweet Adeline."

M. C. Good. Listen again. (*Mendelssohn's "Wedding March" is played.*) And that?

Mrs. Barton. "Wedding March" by Mendelssohn.

M. C. Fine, Mrs. Barton. Now, the last one. (*The music is "Annie Laurie."*)

Mrs. Barton. That's "Auld Lang"— No, that's not it. It's er—er— No, it's not that. Is it "Long, Long Ago"? No, I know that's not right. Oh, I know. It's— No, no. I'm wrong.

(*The Announcer rings his bell.*)

M. C. I'm so sorry, Mrs. Barton. Time's up. Audience?

GUESTS (*in concert*). "Annie Laurie."

M. C. But, Mrs. Barton, you did so well you shall have the prize anyway as a reward for your efforts, and I shall throw in a gallon of Chanel Number Five.

MRS. BARTON. Thank you, doctor. (*Returns to her seat.*)

ANNOUNCER (*impressively*). And now for the jackpot, the sixty-nine-dollar question. Let me tell you what the amazing prizes are for this question, all made possible by the amazing generosity of the United Benevolent Order of Junk Dealers, Inc.

(*The guests applaud.* M. C. *and* ANNOUNCER *take up lists.*)

M. C. Waiting for the lucky winner, we have a fully equipped yacht with captain and crew, nylon masts and booby hatches—I mean ruby hatches.

ANNOUNCER. A dude ranch in the Canadian Rockies, with mounties, bears, and everything.

M. C. A new seven-passenger, fluid-drive, Cadiford car, with needlepoint cushions and, instead of a horn, chimes that play "Nearer, My God, to Thee."

ANNOUNCER. A three months' trip to Indonesia, all expenses paid.

M. C. A ticket to the world-series games for the next twenty seasons.

ANNOUNCER. A sable coat with a mink collar.

M. C. A deed to the Brooklyn Bridge, giving you complete ownership.

ANNOUNCER. Five hundred cases of club soda, seven hundred twenty-three cans of spinach; a carload of precooked hams, and a deep-freeze unit.

M. C.   A scholarship to Oxford University.

ANNOUNCER.   Two tickets to— (*names the title of season's most popular play or musical comedy.*)

M. C.   A thousand-foot garden hose and a silver-plated sprinkler.

ANNOUNCER.   A check for one thousand sixty-nine dollars.

M. C.   A first mortgage on the Chase National Bank.

ANNOUNCER.   Three dozen white orchards—I mean orchids.

M. C.   A pipe organ, to be installed wherever you wish.

ANNOUNCER.   Er—er—seems to me something new was added this morning.   I can't think what it was.

M. C.   There *was* something else.   We mentioned the fur coat—

ANNOUNCER.   Yes, and the dude ranch.

M. C.   I remember!   Friends, our sponsors have, out of the great kindness of their hearts, added one more wonderful gift.

ANNOUNCER.   One more wonderful gift.

M. C.   It is an eight-passenger airplane, a pilot's license, and a marble hangar.   The plane is the latest invention of Ezekiel Elgin, the man who has given the world so many delightful inventions—and some day one of them will work.

ANNOUNCER.   With the plane goes, also, a silver helmet, a chest of tools, a life preserver, a barrel of arnica, and a dozen boxes of adhesive tape.

(*The guests applaud loudly.*)

ANNOUNCER.   And now our master of ceremonies, your good friend, Dr. Webster, will ask the question once and only once.   When you came in, you were given paper and pencil. Write the answer as soon as you hear the question. Remember, the United Benevolent Order of Junk Dealers, Inc., wishes you luck.

M. C. If any of you suffer from a weak heart or high blood pressure, I advise you to leave now. (*Every guest stiffens and looks scared but no one leaves. Each takes out paper and pencil. M. C. solemnly reads from the slip of paper.*) Ready. Listen. On which side of a pitcher is the handle? (*Silence. Only* MR. GRANT *writes anything. All the others wrinkle their brows and bite their nails. Bell is rung by the* ANNOUNCER.) Time's up. How many have an answer? (MR. GRANT *raises his hand. M. C. is surprised and annoyed.*) Oh, so you have an answer, Mr. Grant. Well, well, that's just fine—if it proves to be correct. Tell me, Mr. Grant: On which side of a pitcher is the handle?

(*The others lean forward anxiously to hear answer.*)

MR. GRANT. On the outside, of course. Any dope knows that!

(*The other contestants faint.*)

M. C. (*stunned*). It's right! I can't believe it. Bring me your paper. (MR. GRANT *brings the paper to the* M. C., *who looks at the written answer.*) It's right! That's fine! Just fine! Mr. Grant, you have won—(*reads from the list*)—a yacht, a dude ranch, a Cadiford car, a trip to Indonesia, a ticket to the world series for twenty seasons—(MR. GRANT *sinks to the floor, overcome. M. C. continues*)—a sable coat, the Brooklyn Bridge, a scholarship to Oxford, a pipe organ—a—a (*falters*)—an—air—an air! Give me air! (M. C. *faints.*)

ANNOUNCER. You have just heard "The Numbers

Game" on Station OOO, through the courtesy of the United Benevolent Order of Junk Dealers, Inc. Tune in again next Thursday evening. This is your announcer, Ken Ross, wishing you all good night. (*He faints.*)

CURTAIN

THE BRIDE DOES HER SHOPPING

(*Across a small table to represent a counter the bride and the clerk converse. She has large basket in which are packages.*)

SHE. A pound of steak, please.

HE. Round?

SHE. I don't care what shape it is so long as it's tender.

HE. How about some alligator pears?

SHE. I haven't an alligator,—not even a goldfish.

HE. What else, lady?

SHE. Animal crackers, please.

HE. No animal crackers. I have dog biscuit.

SHE. Fine. Now, a dozen eggs.

HE. Shall I put them in a box?

SHE. Well I certainly wasn't going to roll them home. I want some apples.

HE. Baldwins?

SHE. Of course. Who wants apples with hair on them?

(*Clerk falls to floor in a faint and she walks out angrily.*)

VIRUS V
(*A television travesty*)
FOR TWELVE MEN AND EIGHT WOMEN

CHARACTERS

MR. SMITH, *owner of the television set*
MRS. SMITH, *his wife*
SALLY SMITH
SAM SMITH } *their children*
MR. BROWN
MRS. BROWN } *neighbors*
BETTY BROWN
BILLY BROWN } *their children*
MR. JONES
MRS. JONES } *more neighbors*
JENNY JONES
JIMMY JONES } *their children*
TASMINE JUKES
MR. BEENE
PIKE
ANNOUNCER
GARTHER ODDFREY } *television performers*
GENE ROGERS
MARY MORTON
BARRY SADDLER

TIME—*Any evening.*

PLACE—*The Smith home.*

SCENE: *Living room of the Smith home, with doors at right and left respectively. The right door leads to the rear of the house and the left to the front hall.*

At center back and along the left wall are chairs and a sofa so arranged that all face the television set. It stands at right, facing left at such an angle that the audience can see only the frame, which looks impressive. Back of it stands a large screen, which conceals from the audience the television performers and the secret door in the right wall by which they enter from the wings and exeunt on cue. Their voices are heard but they are unseen by the audience. Other furnishings may be added to dress the stage as desired.

At the rise of the curtain, the stage is unoccupied, but Mrs. Smith *enters at once at right and arranges the chairs and sofa so that they are in rows like theater seats. As she works,* Mr. Smith *enters at left.*

Mr. Smith. What's the big idea?

Mrs. Smith. Well, somebody always comes in to see the show——

Mr. Smith. They've got a nerve. Let 'em buy television sets of their own.

Mrs. Smith. Now, John.

Mr. Smith (*waxing eloquent*). I paid for the blamed thing, didn't I?

Mrs. Smith (*gently*). You're making your payments promptly.

Mr. Smith (*continuing*). I'd like to sit alone in peace and look at the show I want to see——just once! And another thing, Carrie Smith, from now on, the children are going to bed at eight, no matter who's on the screen. Their school work is getting poorer and poorer; and no wonder. All they think of is Skipalong Rafferty and Whoopdedoodledoody.

Mrs. Smith. Now, John——

MR. SMITH (*interrupts*). If anybody rings the door-bell tonight, don't let 'em in. Tonight I'm going to see the Detective Drama all through without interruption.

MRS. SMITH. Yes, dear. (*Goes off at right.*)

(MR. SMITH *goes to the set and fumbles at the knobs.*)

MR. SMITH. Let's see. Channel 4.

(*He turns on the set and sits comfortably in the best chair. Voices come from back of the set and screen.*)

ANNOUNCER (*speaking from the set*). —presenting the Detective Drama, "The Corpse in the Coffee Pot."

JASMINE (*voice from the set*). He's been missing over a year, Mr. Beene, and I'm getting worried about him. You're a tracer of lost persons. Well, my husband's lost. Trace him.

MR. BEENE (*voice from the set*). His occupation, Mrs. Jukes?

JASMINE. His what? Oh, you mean, what did he do? Nothing and very little of that.

MR. BEENE. Money?

JASMINE. Listen, brother. Why do you think I married him?

MR. BEENE. Enemies?

JASMINE. Only me.

MR. BEENE. When did you last see him, Mrs. Jukes?

JASMINE. It was exactly one year ago last March seventh, on my birthday. We were having coffee here in the living room. I told him he'd given me a diamond necklace for my birthday gift. When I handed him the bill, he flew into a horrible rage. I burst into tears and went upstairs; and that's the last time I ever saw Jerry.

Mr. Beene. Mrs. Jukes, where is the coffee pot you used that evening?

Jasmine. The—the coffee pot?

Mr. Beene (*sternly*). Yes, Jasmine Jukes, the coffee pot.

Jasmine (*worried*). Why—why—in the kitchen, I suppose. I haven't used it since.

Mr. Beene. Why not?

Jasmine. Er—because—because it's too large for one person.

Mr. Beene. Mrs. Jukes, I want that coffee pot at once. (*Thud as of a falling body.*) She's fainted. Pike, come in and pick her up. Then call the police.

Pike (*voice from set*). Yes, Mr. Beene.

(*The doorbell rings off left. Voices all talking at once are heard. Mr. Smith turns off set, then turns it back on low. There is a faint murmur of voices.*)

Mr. Smith (*aloud to himself*). I won't stand it!

Mr. and Mrs. Brown, Billy, *and* Betty *enter at left.*

Mr. Brown. Hi, Smith. We just dropped in to see the fights.

(*All take seats.*)

Mrs. Brown. Now, Ben, don't be selfish. I want to see the fashion show.

Billy. Aw, shucks! I want to see Six-Gun Gus.

Betty (*crying*). I want to see Ukla, Gran, and Mollie.

Mr. Smith (*politely, with venom*). Don't let me keep

you waiting. Just make up your minds. That's all I ask.

> SALLY *and* SAM SMITH *enter at left.*

SAM. Daddy, did you say we had to go to bed at eight?
SALLY. It isn't fair. I've got to see Whoopdedoodledoody. All the rest in my class do.
SAM. Daddy, I can't sleep if I don't see Skipalong Rafferty.

> MRS. SMITH *enters at right.*

MRS. SMITH (*to* SALLY *and* SAM). Sit down, children. You may stay up tonight. After that, we'll see.
MR. SMITH. You're darned right, we'll see!

(*From the television set comes the sound of a shot, then silence.*)

MR. BROWN. Well, whatever that was, it's over. How's about the fights?

(MR. SMITH *turns off the set.*)

MRS. BROWN (*hopefully*). Fashion Show?
BETTY. Ukla, Gran and Mollie. That's educational, my teacher says.
BILLY. Six-Gun Gus. Who wants education? Give me action.

SALLY. Whoopdedoodledoody.
SAM. You're all crazy. Skipalong Rafferty.
MRS. SMITH (*hopefully*). How about the circus?

That's on Channel 11.

ALL THE CHILDREN (*in concert, grudgingly*). Well—

MR. SMITH. All right. The circus. (*Turns on the set.*)

(*The music of the march, "Barnum and Bailey's Favorite," is heard. A record may be used.*)

ALL THE CHILDREN. A-ah!

SALLY. Aren't the seals darling!

SAM. Look at that clown!

BILLY. Elephants! Gosh!

BETTY. Ponies! When I grow up, I'm gonna be a circus rider.

BILLY. You couldn't ride a velocipede.

BETTY (*tearfully*). Mother, make Billy stop saying mean things to me.

MRS. BROWN. Sh-h! Look at the lions.

(*From the set comes roar of lions and the shrieks of the crowd. These sounds may be imitated by the director and his assistants.*)

BETTY. Maybe I'll be a lion tamer.

BILLY. You've got such a swelled head you couldn't get it in a lion's mouth.

BETTY (*crying again*). Mother, make Billy stop!

SAM. Wow! Look at the trapeze artists!

(*All lean forward eagerly.*)

BILLY. Gosh!

(*From the set comes a loud, awed "A-ah!"*)

SALLY. I thought she was gonta fall.

BILLY. Gosh!

BETTY. It scares me.

BILLY. Don't look then.

From the set comes loud applause and lively music just as MR. *and* MRS. JONES, JIMMY, *and* JENNY *enter at left.*

MR. JONES. Hello, folks. We just walked in. Didn't want to interrupt. How's about seeing the fights?

MRS. JONES (*as the Jones family find their seats*). No, the fashion show.

MRS. BROWN. That's what I say.

MR. BROWN. The fights.

JIMMY. The Mystery Man.

JENNY. The Fairy Tale Lady.

THE OTHER FOUR CHILDREN (*in concert*). Fairy tales! They're old-fashioned.

SALLY. I want Whoopdedoodledoody.

SAM. Skipalong Rafferty.

BETTY. Ukla, Gran, and Mollie.

BILLY. Six-Gun Gus.

MR. SMITH. The circus is over. (*Turns the set off.*) Make up your minds. That's all I ask.

MRS. SMITH (*timidly*). There's a lovely symphony orchestra on Channel 2 in just a few minutes.

MR. JONES. I don't like to hear musicians, let alone look at 'em.

MR. BROWN. Me, either. Give me a good fight.

MR. JONES. Me, too.

MR. SMITH. I can't please you all—as if I care! So here's a brand new program on Channel 6.

ALL THE OTHERS (*in concert*). What is it?

MR. SMITH (*grimly*). Listen and learn. (*Turns on the set. All listen with varied expressions, mostly disgusted ones.*) Listen and learn.

ODDFREY (*speaking from the set*). Good evening, everybody. This is your old friend, Garthur Oddfrey, and His Talent Show.

ALL THE CHILDREN (*in concert, crossly*). A-aw!

ALL THE PARENTS (*in concert*). Keep still. Maybe it's good.

ALL THE CHILDREN (*in concert*). It won't be.

(*From the set comes music of march, "On Parade," or anything in march time.*)

BETTY. He's fat. Garthur Oddfrey's fat.

SAM. Lookit! He's chewin' gum.

BILLY (*hopefully*). Wish I had some. Mrs. Smith—?

MRS. SMITH. I'm sorry, Billy. I have no chewing gum.

ODDFREY (*speaking from the set*). Friends, settle back in your rocking chairs, insert a stick of Choose-It Chewing Gum into your big mouths, and prepare to enjoy yourselves.

ANNOUNCER (*from set*). Choose-It Gum—none better. Good for teeth, digestion, and disposition. Now, Garthur Oddfrey, bring on your talent.

ODDFREY. And how! First, I have a young man. What's your name, buddy?

GENE (*from set*). Gene Rogers. I sing cowboy songs.

ODDFREY. O.K., Gene. Sing us one.

(GENE *sings any western song. As he ends, applause is heard from the set.*)

SAM. He ain't as good as Skipalong Rafferty or Roy Autrey.

ODDFREY. And now a pretty girl—Mary Morton. What are you going to do, Mary?

MARY (*from set*). I tap dance, Mr. Oddfrey.

ODDFREY. Tap away, Mary.

(*The sound of tap dancing to any familiar tune comes from the set. Record of dance music may be used. Applause as it ends. Children look bored.*)

ODDFREY. And next a harmonica player. What's your name and what are you going to play?

BARRY (*speaking from the set*). Barry Saddler, sir, and I'm going to play "Smoke Gets in Your Eyes."

(*If the performer can play well, no record will be needed. If he does not play, any record of a leading harmonica player may be used.*)

ALL (*in concert*). Not bad!

SAM. But Skipalong Rafferty's better.

(*During the ensuing lines, the talent show is unheard except for faint strains of music occasionally, followed by applause. Conversation grows louder and louder.*)

MR. BROWN *and* MR. JONES (*in unison*). How's about the fights?

MRS. BROWN *and* MRS. JONES (*in unison*). The fashion show?

BETTY. Ukla, Gran, and Mollie.

BILLY. Six-Gun Gus.

JENNY. The Fairy Tale Lady.

JIMMY. The Mystery Man.

SALLY. Whoopdedoodledoody.

SAM. Skipalong Rafferty.

ALL THE OTHER CHILDREN (*in concert*). Aw!

Sam (*angrily*). Whose television set is this, anyway?

Mrs. Smith (*aroused at last*). He's right! Sam's right! (*She rushes to the set and shuts it off.*) I'm sorry, folks. After all, it *is* *our* television set and, though we may seem selfish, we—we'd like to hear the programs we prefer, once in a while. I'm turning on the symphony orchestra. If you people don't like it, that's just too bad. My children are going to bed.

Mr. Smith. The rest of you can go to— er—your homes!

Mrs. Smith (*politely, with an effort*). If you care to hear the orchestra, we'll be charmed to have you stay.

Mr. Smith. Oh, I don't know. I wouldn't say that!

Mrs. Smith. Sh-h, John!

Mr. *and* Mrs. Brown (*in concert, rising*). Well, really!

Betty (*whining*). Mother, can't I see Ukla, Gran, and Mollie?

Billy. Father, make her turn on Six-Gun Gus.

Mr. Brown (*pathetically*). Son, we're not wanted here—and by our own neighbors, too. It's an ungrateful world—and I had two bucks on one of the fights!

Mr. *and* Mrs. Brown (*in unison, pushing the children ahead of them and going left*). Good night. (*They go off at left with the children.*)

Mrs. Jones (*standing*). Come, James. If I can't see the fashion show, I may as well go home.

Mr. Jones. Fashion show, my eye! I want to see the fights.

Jimmy. I wanta see "The Mystery Man."

Jenny (*sadly*). I haven't missed "The Fairy Tale Lady," not once since Mr. Smith got the television set. It isn't fair.

Mrs. Smith (*sweetly*). You're going to miss it tonight, Jenny.

JIMMY.   And we won't get any sandwiches, either.

JENNY.   Or cookies.   (*Cries.*)

MR. *and* MRS. JONES (*in unison*).   Come, children.
(*They stalk toward left.*)   Good night, friends.   (*They
say "friends" with a very disagreeable inflection as they
exeunt left.*)

SALLY.   Hurry up, mother.   Turn it on.   There's
just time for "Whoopdedoodledoody."

SAM.   Don't be a pig, Sally.   Mother, turn on Skipalong Rafferty.

MRS. SMITH (*firmly*).   You two children go straight
to bed, unless you want to listen to the orchestra.

SAM *and* SALLY (*in unison*).   Aw, mother!

MRS. SMITH.   Then it's bed.

SALLY.   No cookies?

SAM.   No sandwiches?

MRS. SMITH (*sweetly*).   No, just bed.

SAM *and* SALLY (*in concert, meekly, knowing they
have met their match*).   Yes, mother.   Good night,
mother.   Good night, father.

MR. SMITH.   Good night, children.

MRS. SMITH.   Good night.   Sleep well.

(*The children go sadly off at left.*)

MR. SMITH.   My dear, don't you think you were—er
—just a bit severe on our guests?

MRS. SMITH.   It's what you wanted, isn't it?

MR. SMITH.   Yes, but—

MRS. SMITH.   Then be thankful I had the g—er—
stamina to do it.   You didn't.   And Sam and Sally are
settled, too.

MR. SMITH.   You're right, as usual, my dear.   Now,
I'll just bring in the sandwiches and cookies.   If you'll
make some coffee, I'll enjoy the fights in peace and quiet
for once.

Mrs. Smith (*sweetly*). You make the coffee, dear, and I'll listen to the symphony.

Mr. Smith. Wh-what did you say?

Mrs. Smith (*as before*). You heard me. Put the coffee on, dear.

Mr. Smith (*stunned*). Yes—yes, dear.

Mr. Smith goes off at right. She turns on the set. Music of "Finlandia" by Sibelius or any similar record fills the room. She smiles contentedly, leans back in the easiest chair, and closes her eyes. Mr. Smith appears in the right doorway, looks at her, shakes his head in bewilderment, and goes back to the kitchen off right as

The Curtain Falls

MOONRISE ISLAND
(*A radio farce*)

FOR FOUR MEN, FIVE WOMEN, AND EXTRAS

CHARACTERS

JANE JOHNSON, *a budding radio playwright*
GUEST
OFFSTAGE VOICES FROM THE RADIO
  ANNOUNCER
  FATHER
  MOTHER   } *players in "Moonrise Island"*
  CICELY
  CLYDE
  STRANGE WOMAN }
  POLICEMAN   } *players in the gangster play*
SEVERAL GUESTS, SOUND EFFECTS MAN OFFSTAGE

TIME—*Evening.*

PLACE—*Jane's home.*

SCENE: *Living room of the Johnson home. At center back stands a large radio. Behind it and at sides up right and left are tall screens, back of which sit the radio performers, the announcer, and the sound effects man. All of these players are invisible to the audience. The radio will light up when turned on, but is set at no station. A few chairs are at the right of the radio. Other furnishings may be added, as desired.*

At the rise of the curtain, JANE stands near the radio at left, while several guests occupy the chairs on the opposite side.

JANE. I'm so thrilled to think my little play won first prize in the radio drama contest.

GUEST. How many contestants were there?

JANE (*with dignity*). Four. And now you're about to hear it. Some of my friends are the actors. I typed the script for them myself. I wouldn't let anyone else see it till it gets copyrighted.

(*She turns on the radio and sits, smiling, ready to be thrilled. The radio voices begin to speak.*)

ANNOUNCER. And now it gives us great pleasure to present the prize-winning drama, "Moonrise Island," a tender romance of young love, written by Miss Jane Johnson, of ———— (*insert name of town*). Congratulations, Miss Johnson. The players are all members of Miss Johnson's drama group, and we feel sure their performances will give added luster to her brilliant play. Ladies and gentlemen, "Moonrise Island."

(*Music of Beethoven's "Moonlight Sonata" is heard, then dies away as the play begins.*)

FATHER (*in a quavering voice*). Marthy, mebbe we done wrong a-comin' here to live. Moonrise Island is a lonely spot for a young girl. Cicely's bound to get lonesome.

STRANGE WOMAN (*from the gangster play in a voice rough and tough*). OK., Mike, but you're bound to get arrested for passing bad checks if we go back to civilization.

(*The music of "Moonglow" is softly played.*)

JANE (*horrified*). But that's not in my play—not a woman like that! Somebody got the scripts mixed.

GUESTS (*in concert*). Shh!

(*The radio voices begin again.*)

CICELY (*in a voice young and sweet*). Mother, daddy, the most wonderful thing has happened to me. I can't believe it.

FATHER. Tell us, daughter. Maybe we won't, either.

MOTHER (*gently*). Yes, tell us, dear.

CICELY. I met a wonderful guy (JANE *gasps*)—er— a wonderful gentleman.

FATHER. Now, daughter, I don't want you to be lonesome, but—

CICELY (*interrupts*). I brought him home, daddy. Come in, Clyde. Clyde, these are my parents. Parents, this is Clyde.

CLYDE (*a smooth number*). Your charming daughter dragged me—(JANE *gasps*)—er—I mean desired me to come home with her and meet you. Welcome to Moonrise Island.

STRANGE WOMAN (*from gangster play*). You're not a flatfoot, I hope—for your sake.

JANE. Oh! That's not in my play!

CLYDE. I hope you will not be lonely here. I am the only other resident of the dump—er—of the dunes.

MOTHER. We love it—the beautiful flowers—

FATHER. And the gentle breeze. It was so cold and stormy where we lived before.

(*The sound effect of a hurricane comes from off up center. The wind dies a hurried death as the sound effects man realizes his mistake.*)

CLYDE. When the wind is from the west, you can hear the chapel bells chiming on the mainland.

CICELY (*too sweetly*). I just love chapel bells.

FATHER. I ain't been to chapel in nigh onto thirty years.

(The sound of very loud bells as for fire is heard. It stops suddenly. JANE groans.)

CICELY *(hurriedly repeating herself)*. I just love chapel bells.

CLYDE. And, Cicely, I think I'm beginning to loath—— to love you.

CICELY. Oh, Clyde, this is so sudden.

MOTHER *and* FATHER *(in concert)*. But very pleasing.

CLYDE. First, before I go to the mainland to purchase an engagement ring. I hope I have enough money with me.

CICELY. Don't bother to buy anything expensive. Just a small diamond will do—say, two carats—I mean, too, care for you, and for you to care for me is all that matters.

STRANGE WOMAN. I hate a cheapskate.

JANE *(covering her face with her hands)*. O-oh!

CLYDE *(continuing)*. First I must tell you the history of Moonrise Island. It was settled years ago by my great-grandfather, who came here from Indiana.

(Sound effect of Indians on the warpath, such as galloping ponies and war whoops.)

JANE. This is awful! I can't bear it! It should sound like a wagon train.

CLYDE. He saw the island, gleaming like a pearl in the mellow light of the rising moon. So he decided to remain here, away from the harsh realities of the busy world—

STRANGE WOMAN. Of course his being wanted for a train robbery had nothing to do with it.

CLYDE *(unheeding, since he does not hear the voice)*. And he named it Moonrise Island.

CICELY. How romantic!

CLYDE. But not more so than our meeting today, Cicely.

MOTHER *and* FATHER (*in concert*). Ain't it the truth!

STRANGE WOMAN. I always say, give me the riches and to heck with romance.

CLYDE. Listen to the perfect peace of a summer afternoon on Moonrise Island, where no harsh sounds of our so-called civilization break the magic spell. We hear nature's symphony—bird songs, chirping crickets, and the gentle rustle of leaves.

(*The sound effects man gives out with police whistles, shots, shrieks, and groans.*)

STRANGE WOMAN. They've got him. They've got Mike!

(*Music of "Moonlight Sonata" again.*)

JANE. This is incredible! I'll—I'll sue somebody.

(*"Moonlight Sonata" grows louder, then dies away.*)

FATHER (*happily*). At last we've found us a quiet spot to end our days in, mother.

MOTHER. And Cicely's got a good husband to end her days with, pa.

FATHER. Yes, she sure has.

STRANGE WOMAN. How much moolah's he got? That's what I want to know. What's his bank account? Tell me that.

CICELY. Clyde dear?

CLYDE. Yes, Cicely darling?

Cicely. I wonder if you're as happy as I am?
Father *and* Mother (*in concert*). Or as we are.

(*Sound effects man blows police whistles.*)

Policeman (*from the gangster play*). Drop that gun, Gatti. This is it!

(*The music of "Prisoner's Song" is heard, switching abruptly to "Moonglow," and then stopping with a jerk.*)

Jane (*glaring at radio*). It's all mixed up—words and music and everything! And it was such a sweet play! I'll sue somebody! And my own players didn't even read the words correctly. I know I don't type well—but— (*Bursts into tears.*)

(*The radio comes on again.*)

Announcer. Ladies and gentlemen, we interrupt this program to apologize—
Jane (*fiercely*). I should think you would.
Announcer (*continuing*). —for crossed wires or something which gave you two dramas badly mixed up—Miss Jane Johnson's prize-winning "Moonrise Island," and the weekly installment of "Horror, Inc." on GYC. Today's installment was called "Mike McGinnis Meets His Match." Tune in again next week—er—I mean—please accept our sincere apologies. This evening we shall broadcast the drama that won second prize, "Stars Over Somaliland," by Harvey H. Homespun.

Jane (*turning the radio off with force*). Second prize phooey! (*She bursts into violent weeping as*)

THE CURTAIN FALLS

WILLOUGHBY'S WINDOW
FOR FIVE MEN AND TEN EXTRA WOMEN

CHARACTERS

WILLOUGHBY, *window trimmer in a department store*
PERRINE ⎫
CLERK ⎬ *other employees of the store*
SLIM ⎫
TIM ⎬ *two crooks*
TEN BEAUTIFUL MODELS

TIME—*The present.*

PLACE—*The street in front of a department store.*

COSTUMES AND CHARACTERISTICS.—Willoughby is an earnest young man who abhors modern feminine attire. Perrine is a jovial chap. All the men wear plain business suits. The models wear very attractive but modest party dresses. Skirts are long enough to conceal their feet and the fact that they wear no stockings and have bathing slippers on their feet. Under the party dresses, brief, up-to-date bathing suits in gay colors are worn. If desired, caps to match the suits may be concealed under the party dresses. The men of the play wear plain business suits.

SCENE: *The stage is set to represent a show window in a store, with a public sidewalk in front of it. Entrances are at right and left. The window may be made by placing a long platform in the center of the stage and erecting a beaverboard frame eight or ten feet high in front of it. Or the frame could be indicated by running a railing around the platform. The window is*

*tastefully trimmed for a contest, and down in one corner
is a small sign reading "Willoughby." Back of the
window are dark curtains that open in the middle.*

At the rise of the curtain, WILLOUGHBY *and* PERRINE
*enter at left and stroll in front of the window, where
they pause.*

PERRINE. All finished, I see, Willoughby.

WILLOUGHBY. Yes, Mr. Perrine. I think it's beautiful. Don't you?

PERRINE. Not bad. But the judges don't appreciate
high art. As I told you this morning they'd rather see
bathing beauties any day. That's the way to win a
prize: give the judges what they like, not what they
ought to like.

WILLOUGHBY (*proudly*). My sign will never be seen
in a window containing a vulgar display, if I never win
a prize.

PERRINE. Well, I wish you luck, Willoughby. You'll
need it. Well, I must go home. Tomorrow morning
before the store opens· the judges will be around and
award the blue ribbon.

WILLOUGHBY (*wishfully*). A-ah!

PERRINE. And also a check for one thousand bucks
to the lucky window trimmer. Good night, Willoughby.
(*Walks off right.*)

(WILLOUGHBY *walks around and inspects his window
from every angle, looking pleased. At last he goes off
right.*)

(*The music of* "All Through the Night" *begins. The
models come to life, one by one. They look at each*

*other, smile, and unfasten their dresses, dropping them
to the floor and revealing their gay bathing suits. They
pull out caps, adjust them at a jaunty angle, nod at
each other, and walk gayly off through black curtains
up center.)*

*As the music dies away, SLIM and TIM enter at right.
They stop in front of the window.*

SLIM. Funny! An empty window. Thought there
was a contest in this store.
TIM. Look, Slim—dresses. Dresses on the floor.
SLIM. Yeah, Tim. We could sell 'em if we had 'em.
TIM. Yeah. Let's get 'em. I know where there's
an unlocked door.

*(They run off right and in a moment appear in the
window through the black curtains, gather up dresses,
and exeunt through the curtain at the back. The music
becomes something gay—"Ciribiribin" or "Don't Fence
Me In," then changes to "Three O'Clock in the Morning.")*

*The models reënter up center, looking very happy.
As they come through the black curtain, they stop in
dismay. No dresses! After searching in corners and in
back of the curtain, they shake heads despairingly. Offstage a clock strikes five. Models look at one another
in alarm and take former poses, in their bathing suits.
They look very beautiful. The curtain falls, to indicate
the lapse of three hours. After a few minutes, it rises
to the music of the round, "Merrily, Merrily." It is
now eight A. M. and the scene is unchanged except that
on WILLOUGHBY'S sign in the window is fastened the
coveted blue ribbon and a gold star.*

At the rise of the curtain, PERRINE *enters at right and stares at the window in amazement.*

PERRINE (*aloud to himself*). Well, I'll be—! I never— (*He sees the bathing beauties.*) I never thought he had it in him. He came back and changed the window!

Enter WILLOUGHBY *at right, looking despondent.*

WILLOUGHBY. Well, who got it?
PERRINE. Willoughby, come here. Look. First prize! You're a wise chap.
WILLOUGHBY (*seeing only the bathing suits, which shock him*). Who did that? It's—it's sabotage!
PERRINE. It's first prize. Look. And a thousand bucks!
WILLOUGHBY (*overcome*). First prize? But—but I didn't do it! Where are the dresses?
PERRINE. Willoughby, you're keeping something from me. Why didn't you tell me you have a fairy godmother?
WILLOUGHBY. Who did it?
PERRINE. What do you care? It's a darned good window.
WILLOUGHBY (*beginning to realize his luck*). First prize!
PERRINE. And a thousand bucks.

Enter CLERK *at left, carrying an armload of dresses.*

CLERK. We found these in the alley, Mr. Perrine. The thieves must have been scared away. Swell window, Willoughby. Congratulations! I never knew you went in for bathing beauties.

WILLOUGHBY. I—er—I didn't (*boldly*), but I think from now on, I shall.

(*The models look at him, smile sweetly, and wink as*)

THE CURTAIN FALLS

LOVE'S YOUNG DREAM

(*A young man and a young woman sit on the sofa, talking.*)

SHE. When did you first know you loved me?

HE. When I got mad because folks said you were as dumb as you are homely. If you loved me, why did you refuse me at first?

SHE. Just to see what you would do.

HE. I might have rushed right off.

SHE. I had the door locked. When you told Dad we were engaged, did you tell him you had $5000 in the bank?

HE. Yes.

SHE. What did he do then?

HE. He borrowed it.

SHE. Darling, do you believe in allowances for married women?

HE. Surely. I think a husband should make allowances for a lot of things.

SHE. Do you realize, Henry, you are a dentist and I am a manicurist? We should never marry, never!

HE. Why not, for Pete's sake?

SHE. If we ever fight it will be tooth and nail.

IN THE DOCTOR'S OFFICE

FOR FOUR MEN AND ONE WOMAN

CHARACTERS
FAKE DOCTOR
PATIENT
NURSE
REAL DOCTOR
INTERNE

COSTUMES.—The fake doctor, real doctor, and patient wear plain business suits. The fake doctor's suit is shabby. The nurse and interne wear white uniforms.

PROPERTIES.—For fake doctor: two signs reading, "Watch your coat and hat" and "Count your change. No money refunded"; suitcase containing hammers, saws, awls, bandages, a small stick, key attached to a string, iron bar.

SCENE: *A doctor's office. There are two doors at right and left respectively. Up center against the backdrop is a large desk and chair, with a straight-backed chair beside the desk. On the desk are instruments, books, a filing box, etc. Several other chairs are scattered about the room. Other furniture may be added as desired.*

At the rise of the curtain, the stage is unoccupied. Immediately FAKE DOCTOR *enters at left carrying two large signs and a suitcase. He sets the signs on chairs so that they are plainly visible to the audience. One reads, "Watch your hat and coat" and the other, "Count your change. No money refunded." He opens the suitcase and takes out hammers, saws, awls, etc., and drops them on the desk up center. The* NURSE, *whose spotless uniform contrasts sharply with the shabby, unkempt appearance of* FAKE DOCTOR, *opens the right door and starts to enter, sees the* FAKE DOCTOR, *whose back is to her, and runs off right, without being seen by him.*

PATIENT *enters at left, and taking the man for the doctor, addresses him.*

PATIENT.   Doctor, I want a complete checkup.
FAKE DOCTOR.   Why not?   Take off your coat and sit down.   Roll up your sleeve.

(PATIENT *sits in the chair at front of the stage, and does as directed.* FAKE DOCTOR *wraps a bandage about his arm, twists the bandage tight with a small stick, as if it were a tourniquet, takes a bicycle pump from the pile of tools on the table and works it vigorously, making a swishing noise, which really comes from offstage and results from rubbing papers together and rubbing sandpaper over a board.*)

FAKE DOCTOR (*as he stops pumping and removes the bandage*).   Blood pressure 362.
PATIENT.   O-oh!
FAKE DOCTOR.   Now I'll test your heart.   (*He slips a key, attached to a string, down the patient's shirt front and listens.   A violent knocking, loud and persistent, comes from offstage, where wood is hit with a hammer in steady rhythm.*)   Bad.   Now the lungs. (FAKE DOCTOR *bends over* PATIENT *and taps his chest with an iron bar.   There is a loud gurgling sound, made offstage by pouring water out of a large bottle with a*

small neck.) Bad, very bad! Now, your brain. (FAKE
DOCTOR *taps* PATIENT's *head with a small hammer.
There is a loud buzzing and the sound of turning wheels,
made by an electric drill or, preferably, a vacuum cleaner
attached and turned on in the wings.*) Brain nearly
gone. Skull empty! Now your knees. (FAKE DOCTOR
hits the PATIENT *on the knee, and the sound of running water is heard. It is made by pouring water from
a pitcher into a pan offstage.* FAKE DOCTOR *hurriedly
pulls off the* PATIENT's *shoes.*) Water on the knee!
You'll have to wear pumps. Now—er—that's all.

PATIENT (*faintly*). But what shall I do?

FAKE DOCTOR (*surprised*). Do? Nothing. You're
in perfect condition.

The PATIENT *slithers to the floor in a dead faint.
The door at right opens, and in rush the* NURSE, *the*
REAL DOCTOR, *and an* INTERNE *in uniform from a
near-by mental hospital.*

NURSE. There's the man, doctor. He's crazy.

INTERNE. You're telling me! He escaped from the
violent ward an hour ago.

REAL DOCTOR. Good work, nurse.

INTERNE (*kindly, to the* FAKE DOCTOR). Come along,
Mr. Wayne. It's dinner time.

FAKE DOCTOR. No wonder I've been feeling so
strange. I'm hungry. (*He puts his tools back into
his suitcase, picks it up, puts his signs under his arm
and goes off at left, followed by the* INTERNE, *who
waves a cheerful farewell to the* NURSE *as he goes.*)

PATIENT (*coming to and sitting up*). What happened?

REAL DOCTOR. It's all right. He's an escaped
lunatic.

PATIENT.   But those tests he made! I heard the awful sounds!

NURSE.   Sounds?

PATIENT.   Yes, my heart and my head!

NURSE (*smiling*).   Listen!

(*From offstage come the noises heard before, singly and then all at once. Then they cease as suddenly as they began.*)

PATIENT.   Why, that's what I heard!

NURSE.   Plumbers working next door.

CURTAIN

THE SIGN ON THE DOOR

FOR FOUR MEN, ONE WOMAN, AND EXTRAS

CHARACTERS

BILL ⎱
JOE ⎰ *workmen*

GIRL ⎱
BOY ⎰ *ballet pupils*

CHUCK BLUNT, *an athletic coach*
ANY NUMBER OF DANCE PUPILS

TIME—*About nine A. M.*

PLACE—*A studio*

COSTUMES.—The workmen wear overalls and caps. The dance pupils wear slacks, blouses, and ballet slippers and look very, very artistic. Blunt wears a sweater and slacks and looks like a prize fighter.

PROPERTIES.—For Bill and Joe, a sign apiece, one of which reads, "Chuck Blunt, Athletic Coach." Signs should be of suitable size for being tacked on a door.

SCENE: *An empty-looking studio, with one door at right. It has some gymnasium equipment, including punching bags and ropes hanging on a frame at the back. A stool stands at left.*

Before the curtain rises, BILL *and* JOE *enter at right, each carrying a sign under his arm, and stroll across the stage in front of the curtain.*

BILL. Hurry up. Got to get these signs up before

the joints open.

JOE.   Yeah.   Almost nine now.

(*They go off at left.*)

(*The curtain rises on the studio, and immediately the ballet pupils enter at right.   They stop and survey the room disparagingly.*)

GIRL.   This is a desolate-looking place.
BOY.   It doesn't inspire me.

(*They practice a few pirouettes, etc., while waiting. They stiffen to attention as the door opens at right and* BLUNT *enters.   The pupils bow.*)

PUPILS (*in concert*).   Good morning, professor.   We are your new class.

BLUNT (*looking at them with violent disapproval*). Professor?   That's a new one.   Come on.   No time to waste.   None of you look like much.   Get in line.   Step lively.   (*Pupils look astonished at his gruff voice and manner.*)   Get in line, I said.   Heads up, stomachs in, eyes front.   For heaven's sake, show some pep!

(*The pupils stand in a row facing front.   After this, they obey directions but grow visibly weaker as time goes on.*)

BLUNT.   Join hands.   Circle.   Move to left.   Fast. Faster!

GIRL.   No music?

BLUNT.   Music!   What d'you think this is?   To right.   Faster, faster!   (*They obey.*)   Drop hands. Straight line.   Heads right.   Heads left.   Drop on stomachs—flat.

PUPILS (*hesitating to obey the last order*). O-oh!

BLUNT. Drop! You heard me! (*They drop.*) Now, roll over. (*They roll.*) You don't have to play dead. You're that way already, but I'll put some life into you. Up. (*They struggle to their feet.*) Arms up. Stretch. (*They stretch.*) Higher, higher, higher! O.K. Drop 'em. (*They do, nearly dropping themselves.*) Kick to left. (*They kick.*) Kick to right. Join hands in circle. Run right. Run left. Faster! Faster. Faster! O.K. Drop hands. Stand still, sissies! (*The pupils pant heavily and mop their brows.* BLUNT *drags the stool at left down center.*) Line up. Jump over the stool. (*They do.*) O.K. (*He kicks the stool to one side.*) Line up. Drop on stomachs. (*The pupils drop as if nearly dead.* BLUNT *glares at them.*) Roll over on backs. Kick. Higher, higher, higher! (*They kick.*) O.K. Up! (*With great difficulty, pupils rise and stand in a wavering line.*) Bend. Touch floor with hands and keep those knees straight! (*As they obey, a few of the pupils fall over, but* BLUNT *ignores them.*) O.K. Heads up. Knee bending. Ready. One, two, one, two. (*He keeps on counting till they can't bend knees any more.*) O.K. Stand still, sissies!

BOY (*falteringly*). When—do—we—dance?

BLUNT. Dance? Dance? What do you think this is? A dance studio?

PUPILS (*in concert*). Yes. (*They sink to floor, ex-hausted.*)

BLUNT. Well, of all—!

Enter BILL *and* JOE *at right, each with a sign under his arm.*

BILL. Excuse me, sir. Are you Chuck Blunt?

BLUNT. Yeah. Want to make something of it?

BILL (*embarrassed*). Well—er—we made a mistake, we think. We—er—put the wrong sign on your door.

BLUNT (*menacingly*). You what?

(PUPILS *lift their heads and listen.*)

JOE. Yes, sir. We thought this was Professor Hercule De Dilly's Dance Studio.

BLUNT (*ominously*). What!

JOE. Yes, sir. We put his sign on your door and your sign on his door, but he found out the mistake. Here is your sign. (*Holds the sign out to him.*)

BLUNT (*grabbing the sign and reading it*). Chuck Blunt, Athletic Coach." I oughta sue you!

BILL. We're sorry, sir.

JOE (*taking the sign from him*). We'll fix the signs right away and send your class in. (*He and* JOE *exeunt at right.*)

BLUNT (*to pupils*). Scram, you—you ballet dancers! (*Chuckles.*) I wonder how Hercule made out!

(*The pupils hobble off at right as—*)

THE CURTAIN FALLS

THE CENSUS TAKER
(*A talking act*)
FOR A MAN AND A WOMAN

CHARACTERS
WOMAN
CENSUS TAKER

TIME—*Census year.*

PLACE—*A living room.*

PROPERTIES.—For Census Taker, large notebook, fountain pen, business card. For woman, knitting materials and needles.

SCENE: *Living room in* WOMAN'S *home, with a door at right. It may be furnished in any manner, with at least one armchair and a straight-backed chair, both placed near center.*

At the rise of the curtain, the WOMAN, *who is fair, fat, and at least forty, sits in the armchair knitting. Doorbell rings off right.*

WOMAN (*calling*). Come in.

The CENSUS TAKER, *a timid young man, enters at right, bearing the usual huge notebook.*

CENSUS TAKER (*politely*). Madam, I am the census taker. Do you wish to see my credentials? (*He holds out the card which he has taken from his pocket.*)

WOMAN: Never mind, young man. I have a trust-
ing nature. Sit down. You must be tired. Are you
naturally nosey, or do you like to learn about other
people? I'll bet you meet some queer ones.

CENSUS TAKER. Well— (*Sits, opens the notebook,
and takes out pen.*) What is your full name?

WOMAN. What's your name, young man? I like to
know to whom I'm talking.

CENSUS TAKER. My name is William Watts.

WOMAN. Now, there's a coincidence. When I was
a young girl—longer ago than I care to remember—I
had a beau named William Watts. It couldn't have
been you. Maybe a relative, though. Where did your
folks come from, young man?

CENSUS TAKER (*beginning to worry*). From Missouri, madam, but really I—

WOMAN (*interrupts*). How old are you? You look
awfully young for so responsible a job. Does the
government pay you well? I suppose not; but at least
it's a job. Are you married? (*The young man makes
desperate attempts to get in a question himself, opening
and closing his mouth like a poor fish.*) Any children?
I do hope you're strict with them. Children all are so
spoiled nowadays. Have you been to Mrs. Brown's next
door? If you can get that woman to tell you her age,
it will be nothing short of a miracle. She acts like
twenty, but she looks like sixty. I always say it's a
mistake to conceal your age.

CENSUS TAKER (*gasping*). Madam, I—

WOMAN. Did you have to take an examination to
become a census taker? Was it hard? Do you know
Bobby Bates? He's a census taker, too. The examination couldn't have been very difficult, or he couldn't have
passed it.

CENSUS TAKER (*mopping his brow*). Madam, I—

WOMAN. I almost went to the movies this afternoon. If I had, I'd have missed you, wouldn't I? And then you'd have to come back again. Who's your favorite movie actor? I like ———— and ———— myself. (*Use names of popular movie actors.*) But I suppose you are more interested in the girls. I just love ————. (*Use name of a popular actress*). Don't you?

CENSUS TAKER (*a sob in his voice*). Madam—I—

WOMAN. Do you like television? I don't think much of it, myself. I like just to listen while I knit. I hate to have to watch something, too. Do you think television will ever take the place of movies?

CENSUS TAKER (*stretching out hands imploringly*). Madam—

WOMAN (*continuing*). Where did you buy that tie, if you don't mind my asking? I'd like to get my grandson—I mean my son—one like it. He's in Princeton. What college did you go to, young man?

CENSUS TAKER (*quaveringly*). Madam—

WOMAN. This is my busy day. The woman who collects for the Red Cross is coming this afternoon. I think I'll give her two dollars. Do you suppose I can deduct it from my income tax? How much do you give to the Red Cross, young man?

CENSUS TAKER. Madam, I—I give up!

(*He claps his hat on his head, closes book, puts it under his arm and staggers off at right.*)

WOMAN (*aloud to herself, surprised*). Now I wonder why he did that! Poor boy! I suppose having to get all that information about perfect strangers *is* tiring, and not everyone is as coöperative as I am. (*She knits violently as—*)

THE CURTAIN FALLS

TURNING THE FABLES ON AESOP
FOR TWO MEN, TWO WOMEN, AND NARRATOR

CHARACTERS
NARRATOR
ANNA ANT
GRACIE GRASSHOPPER
BOSS, *a musical comedy director*
JAMES, *his chauffeur*

TIME—*The present.*

PLACE—*A washerwoman's back yard.*

COSTUMES AND CHARACTERISTICS.—Ant, a pleasant-looking girl, wears the same house dress and apron in all three scenes. Grasshopper wears a gay dress in the first two scenes, changing to a stylish and expensive outfit for the third scene. Boss is a pompous-looking, well-dressed man in a business suit. James wears a chauffeur's uniform.

PROPERTIES.—For Grasshopper, a currency bill. For Boss, business card. For James, two large bags of soiled clothes.

SCENE 1
SCENE: *Back yard of* ANNA ANT's *home, with entrances at left and right. Against the backdrop stand the backs of two houses cut from beaverboard. One house bears a card reading "Ant" and the other a card reading "Grasshopper." It is summer, and shrubs and flowers are in the yard. In front of* ANT's *house are a washtub, a clothes basket, and bags of dirty laundry.*

The NARRATOR *steps on from the wing down extreme' right and addresses the audience.*

NARRATOR. If you were taught, as I was, to regard the fables of Aesop as the last word in simple truth and honest fact, you were misled. Take that old familiar story of the ant and the grasshopper. The industrious ant spends the winter of her life in comfort, social security, old age pension, and everything, while the fun-loving grasshopper starves to death. Don't you believe it! It ain't so. I'll show you what actually happened to an ant and a grasshopper with whom I am personally acquainted. (*Exit down right.*)

The curtain rises to show ANT *at the washtub washing clothes. At once* GRASSHOPPER *enters at right.* ANT *does not stop work when she talks.*

GRASSHOPPER. Come and play, Anna Ant. It's too nice a day to work.
ANT. Gracie Grasshopper, I must work every minute in summer to earn money for winter. I'm doing hand laundry for the summer folks at the hotel.
GRASSHOPPER. Winter's a long way off. Look at the new dance I just made up.
ANT. I haven't time and I wish you wouldn't waste your time so.

GRASSHOPPER. After all, it's my time.

(*To any gay tune—Poldini's "Dancing Doll," or something modern—she does a dance, but* ANT *never looks up.*)

CURTAIN

SCENE 2
SCENE: *Same as in* SCENE 1.

NARRATOR *enters down extreme right in front of the curtain.*

NARRATOR.   And a few weeks later the same thing happened again.   (*Exit in the wing down right.*)

The curtain rises, showing ANT *is still washing, with more bags of laundry on the ground.* GRASSHOPPER *enters at right.*)

GRASSHOPPER.   Anna Ant, I know a new dance.   Don't you want to see it?

ANT.   I haven't time.   Do get to work, Gracie Grasshopper, and earn some money.   Think of the long cold winter ahead of us.

GRASSHOPPER.   You think of it.   I'm having too good a time.

To the melody of "Turkey in the Straw," she does a gay dance. ANT *keeps on washing. As she dances,* JAMES *enters at left, carrying a bag of laundry, and puts it down by* ANT. *He stops and watches the dance. Then he beckons off left, and his* BOSS *enters at left and comes to him.*

BOSS.   What is it, James?

JAMES (*points to* GRASSHOPPER).   Look at that dame dance.

(*The two men stand and watch dance. When dance ends,* GRASSHOPPER *smiles at them.* ANT *keeps on washing.*)

BOSS (*to* GRASSHOPPER).   How would you like a job in the chorus of my new Broadway show, "Dancing Through the Years"?

GRASSHOPPER (*carelessly*). All right, I guess, if there isn't too much work.

BOSS. You'll dance.

GRASSHOPPER. That's not work. It's fun.

BOSS (*handing her his card*). Be at this address tomorrow morning at 10:30. The salary is sixty dollars a week, beginning with rehearsals.

GRASSHOPPER. I'll be there.

(*The two men go off at left. Music starts again, and* GRASSHOPPER *dances for a short time. Then she calls to* ANT.)

GRASSHOPPER. Good-bye, Anna Ant.

ANT (*without looking up*). Good-bye.

(*Exit* GRASSHOPPER *at right.*)

CURTAIN

SCENE 3

SCENE: *Same as in previous scenes except that* GRASSHOPPER'S *house no longer has a sign on it.*

Enter NARRATOR *down right before the curtain.*

NARRATOR. Two years later—which makes a liar of Aesop. (*Exit, down right.*)

At the rise of the curtain, ANT *is still washing and looks older and shabbier. She wears the same dress. The chauffeur,* JAMES, *enters at left with a huge bag of laundry. Behind him comes* GRASSHOPPER *in very stylish and expensive clothing.* JAMES *goes off at left.*

GRASSHOPPER. Anna Ant, don't you remember me? I'm Gracie Grasshopper.

ANT (*actually looking up*). I wondered what had

become of you. Is this your laundry?

GRASSHOPPER. Yes. I'm at the hotel for a few days.
Next month I'm to star in a big musical show. I dance
all the time. It's more fun! What have you been
doing since I saw you last? As if I didn't know.

ANT. Worked all summer and counted my pennies
all winter. Everything costs so much.

GRASSHOPPER (*kindly*). Poor Anna Ant! I'll see
that you get all the washing from the hotel this summer.
Remember how I used to dance in this yard? Here,
just a little gift from me to you. (*She puts a bill in*
ANT's *hand and hurries off at right.*)

ANT (*unfolding the bill and looking at it*). Fifty
dollars! I never saw that much money before. (*Re-
gretfully.*) Maybe I should have danced a little.

CURTAIN

Enter NARRATOR *down right before curtain.*

NARRATOR. See what I mean? I think Gracie Grasshopper sort of turned the fables on Aesop. Don't you?
Shall we dance? (*Exit down right, dancing.*)

A TEN-MINUTE WHITEFACE
MINSTREL SHOW

(The performers are seated in a semicircle facing the audience, with the INTERLOCUTOR *and the twelve endmen and endwomen seated on the front row. The* INTERLOCUTOR *sits in the center, with six ends at his left and six at his right. Behind the principals are seated the chorus and the special soloists. The ends are:* JONES, SMITH, GRAY, MARTIN, CLARK, LANE, MRS. BROWN, MISS WARBLE, MISS MARCH, MRS. KENT, BONES, *and* TAMBO. *If preferred, the performers' real names may be substituted for the foregoing names. The dancers,* MISS LIGHTFOOT *and* MR. TAPPER, *sit in the front row of chorus. The* ANNOUNCER *appears only once and that at the beginning of the performance. He and the uniformed guard are the only players who enter from the wings and then leave the stage.)*

At the rise of the curtain, ANNOUNCER *enters from the wings in front of the semicircle, who are already seated on the stage.*

ANNOUNCER *(to the audience).* Friends, you are about to see an old-fashioned amateur minstrel show. Don't throw things at the players. They're doing the best they can with what they've got, which isn't much. *(Exits.)*

(The entire company sing "De Camptown Races.")

INTERLOCUTOR. Mr. Jones, tell me, what is conscience?

JONES. Conscience, Mr. Interlocutor, is the voice that tells you not to do something after you've done it.

INTERLOCUTOR. Miss Warble will now sing for us.

(MISS WARBLE *sings any desired song in any way she chooses.*)

MRS. BROWN. Miss Warble, where did you learn to sing?

MISS WARBLE (*proudly*). I graduated from a correspondence school.

MRS. BROWN. Sister, you sure lost lots of your lessons.

INTERLOCUTOR (*turning to* SMITH, *who is practically lying down*). Mr. Smith, why are you lying down? You told me you never got tired.

SMITH. That's right. I don't. I always stop and rest before I get tired.

GRAY. Mr. Interlocutor, why is a chicken the most useful animal?

INTERLOCUTOR. I don't know. Tell me, Mr. Gray: Why is a chicken the most useful animal?

GRAY. Because you can eat 'em before they're born and after they're dead.

INTERLOCUTOR. Mr. Martin, what does the word "matrimony" mean?

MARTIN. That ain't no word. It's a sentence.

INTERLOCUTOR. Mr. Clark, do you play an instrument of any kind?

CLARK. Only second fiddle—at home.

INTERLOCUTOR. Then you don't run things at your house?

CLARK. Oh, yes. The lawn mower, washing machine, vacuum sweeper, baby carriage, and the errands.

INTERLOCUTOR. Miss March, define an automaton.

MISS MARCH. Er—er— Oh, I know. An automaton is a gent who eats at the automat.

A uniformed guard rushes on at left.

GUARD. Excuse me, but I'm searching for an escaped lunatic. Did he pass this way?

INTERLOCUTOR. What did he look like?

GUARD. Very short, very thin, weighed about three hundred pounds.

INTERLOCUTOR. What! How can a man be short and thin and still weigh three hundred pounds?

GUARD (*crossly*). Don't act so surprised. I told you he was crazy, didn't I? (*Rushes off at right.*)

INTERLOCUTOR. Mrs. Kent, how would you define tact?

MRS. KENT. Tact is the ability to make your guests feel at home when you darned well wish they were.

INTERLOCUTOR. We will now sing "Polly-Wolly-Doodle." (*All sing. At the close of the song, the* INTERLOCUTOR *turns to* BONES.) Mr. Bones, do you think a rabbit's foot really brings good luck?

BONES. I should say so! My wife felt one in my money pocket last night and thought it was a mouse.

INTERLOCUTOR. Is your wife systematic, Mr. Bones?

BONES. Oh, very. She goes on the theory that you can find whatever you want when you don't want it by looking where it wouldn't be if you did want it.

INTERLOCUTOR. Mr. Lane, how is your mother-in-law?

LANE. Just terrible. She's got chronic frontal sinusitis.

INTERLOCUTOR. Where in the world did she get that?

LANE. The ————. (*Mentions the name of a leading magazine.*) She read about it last month.

INTERLOCUTOR. Mr. Tambo, I hear you've been on a trip through the mountains. Did you have any exciting adventures?

TAMBO. Did I have any exciting adventures! I was

mooching along on a narrow mountain trail on a path only six inches wide, with a steep cliff at the left of me and a five-thousand-foot drop on the right of me. I heard a noise and turned around. There was a huge mountain lion chasing me. I began to run like crazy. Then I got to a turn in the path, and what did I see in front of me?

INTERLOCUTOR. I don't know, Mr. Tambo. What did you see in front of you?

TAMBO. In front of me I saw an enormous tiger, growling and lashing his tail!

INTERLOCUTOR. For heaven's sake, Mr. Tambo! What did you do?

TAMBO. What could I do? The tiger ate me.

INTERLOCUTOR. Miss Lightfoot and Mr. Tapper will now do one of their celebrated dances for us.

(*The dancers rise and glare at each other.*)

LIGHTFOOT. I'm never quite sure, Mr. Tapper, whether you took dancing lessons or wrestling lessons.

TAPPER. Miss Lightfoot, a famous critic told me he never saw dancing like yours but once before.

LIGHTFOOT (*pleased*). Oh, yes. When?

TAPPER. Just before the place was raided.'

LIGHTFOOT. You're from the north, aren't you, Mr. Tapper?

TAPPER. Why do you say that?

LIGHTFOOT. You dance as if you had snowshoes on.

TAPPER. Miss Lightfoot, you'd be a marvelous dancer but for two things.

LIGHTFOOT. What two things?

TAPPER. Your feet.

(*They dance to any desired music, smiling sweetly as they bow to the audience and scowling at each other.*)

INTERLOCUTOR. We will close our minstrel show by singing that old favorite, "Dem Golden Slippers."

(*All sing.*)

CURTAIN

AFTER THE DAY'S WORK

(Mr. and Mrs. are talking.)

MR. Don't you think it's time the baby says Daddy?

MRS. I'm not going to tell him who you are till he gets stronger. Hark! I think I heard a mouse squeak.

MR. Well, I'm not going to oil it. Let it squeak.

MRS. I must have a new fur coat this winter, dear. I just can't wear my old squirrel one all my life.

MR. Why not? The squirrels do. You're always wishing for something you haven't got.

MRS. But what else could one wish for? I think I'll go to a palmist and find out about my future—or shall I go to a mind-reader?

MR. Better go to a palmist. You've got a palm.

MRS. When you come home tomorrow night bring something for the rats. I saw two today.

MR. Something for the rats? I will not. If the rats can't eat what we have in the house, let 'em leave.

SOMETHING TO READ

(Four young women are talking.)

FIRST. I wish I had something to read.

SECOND. Read your Bible.

FIRST. I want something to read for pleasure, not duty. Something romantic, exciting, poetic.

THIRD. You'll find all that in the Bible.

FOURTH. Of course you will. Romance—Ruth and Naomi, Rebecca at the Well, The Shepherds and the Star of Bethlehem.

SECOND. For adventure how about Noah and the Ark, the Israelites Crossing the Red Sea, Samson and Delilah?

THIRD. For excitement try the story of Jezebel, David and Goliath, Joseph and His Brethren.

FOURTH. These are just a few of the wonderful stories in the Bible. As for poetry, listen to these quotations.

* Note—The quotations may be written in notebooks the speakers carry.

SECOND. Underneath are the everlasting arms.

FOURTH. I have been a stranger in a strange land.

THIRD. The sun stood still and the moon stayed.

FOURTH. Whither thou goest, I will go; and where thou lodgest, I will lodge; thy people shall be my people, and thy God my God.

SECOND. The Lord is my rock and my fortress and my deliverer.

THIRD. Night, when deep sleep falleth on men.

FOURTH. Thou hast made him a little lower than the angels.

SECOND. Day unto day uttereth speech and night

unto night showeth knowledge.

THIRD. Weeping may endure for a night, but joy cometh in the morning.

FOURTH. A thousand years in Thy sight are but as yesterday when it is past and as a watch in the night.

SECOND. Yet a little sleep, a little slumber, a little folding of the hands to sleep.

THIRD. As cold waters to a thirsty soul, so is good news from a far country.

FOURTH. As the shadow of a great rock in a weary land.

FIRST. I remember some beautiful lines, too. First the blade, then the ear, after that the full corn in the ear. We walk by faith, not by sight. Look upon the rainbow and praise Him that made it. You are right, girls. I'll go home and read my Bible.

IN THE PET SHOP

CHARACTERS

A talkative and not too bright young matron.

The man who owns the pet shop, patient and long-suffering.

The only setting is a desk or table, with a man at the back of it. Sign: "Perkins' Pet Shop." Another sign says: "Books About Animals."

(The man is straightening a pile of books on the table when the woman enters.)

SHE. I want a dog for a pet.

HE. What sort of dog do you prefer, Madam?

SHE. Oh, I don't know. A dachshund I guess. I have six children and they could all pet him at once.

HE. I just sold my last dachshund. How about a canary?

SHE. No. We had a canary but his cage was right by the radio and he learned static. We had to give him away. I did want a dog. We had a dear little doggie. His name was Nero. We lost him.

HE. Did you put an ad in the papers?

SHE. Why, no. The poor little dear can't read. Still I always say animals are more intelligent than people. They aren't superstitious, like we are.

HE. Nonsense! Did you ever know a mouse that would pass a black cat on Friday?

SHE (*looking at the books on the table*). A book about where elephants are found. That's funny. They're so big I didn't suppose they ever got lost. Tell me, Mr. Perkins, why do hens always lay in the day time?

HE. Maybe because at night they're roosters.

SHE (*laughing*). Oh, that's a joke. Well, let me know when you get a dachshund. Call me up.

HE. But I don't know your name.

SHE (*going out*). Oh, I'm in the telephone book.

———

FRIENDLY ADVICE

(Two women are having a heart-to-heart talk.)

MISS A. What sort of husband would you advise me to get?

MRS. B. None. Get a single man and leave the husbands alone.

MISS A. I didn't accept Jim the first time he proposed.

MRS. B. No, honey, you weren't there.

MISS A. Folks say I grow younger every day.

MRS. B. You do. Years ago you were thirty. Now you're only twenty-five.

MISS A. Do you know, the ring of sincerity was in Jim's voice when he told me he loved me.

MRS. B. It should have been in his hand. A ring in the hand is worth two in the voice. *(Changing the subject.)* I had a quiet evening with a good book last night.

MISS A. I'm afraid that's going to happen to me some night, too. Do you know, Jim's just crazy about me?

MRS. B. Don't take too much credit. He was crazy before he ever saw you. You may not believe it, but you're not the only one who has been proposed to lately. I have said "No" to ten different men this summer.

MISS A. Oh, I don't doubt it. What were they selling?

THE FARMER IN THE DELL

(*Two men from town are talking to a farmer, having stopped at his place on their way to town. Their names are* LEE *and* DALE.)

LEE. I see you raise hogs around here. Do they pay better than potatoes or corn?

FARMER. Well, maybe not, but you see, stranger, the hogs don't need no hoein'.

DALE. Did the lack of rain make the wheat short this year?

FARMER. Short? Why, I had to lather my wheat before I could mow it.

LEE. How does the land lie out this way ? (*Pointing to east.*)

FARMER. It ain't the land that lies. It's them real-estate agents.

DALE. Are you bothered by crows?

FARMER. No, siree. I made a scarecrow that frightened every single crow off the farm. But that's nothin'. Last year I made one that scared the crows so bad they brought back the corn they stole the year before. Well, I've got to take my hogs to the woods to eat acorns.

DALE. Why don't you put your pigs in a pen and feed them corn? They'd get fat much faster. It would save time.

FARMER. Aw, what's time to a hog?

LEE. You ought to have a bicycle to get over your farm with.

FARMER. Uh-huh. I'd rather spend my money on a cow.

LEE. Now wouldn't you look silly riding around on a cow!

FARMER. Not half so silly as I'd look tryin' to milk a bicycle.

DALE. By the way, that Jones boy who used to work for you wants me to give him a job. Is he steady?

FARMER. Steady? If he was any steadier he'd be motionless.

LEE. Tell me, sir, on the whole, have times been good for you farmers lately?

FARMER. Tolerable. I had some brush to burn but lightning set fire to the brush pile and saved me the trouble of burnin' it. I had some trees to cut down but a cyclone came along and did it for me.

DALE. Good. What are you going to do now?

FARMER. Not much. Guess I'll just wait for an earthquake to come along and shake the potatoes out of the ground. I always did hate to dig potatoes.

HOME WORK

(*This requires eight girls. One has paper and pencil and is very much worried. The others enter and look at her curiously.*)

FIRST GIRL. Hey, girls, help me with my homework. I have a list of words to define and I'm not to use a dictionary.

SECOND GIRL. O.K. Go ahead. We know everything, or do we?

FIRST GIRL. I'll say the word. You define it, and I'll write down the answer. Define an average man.

SECOND GIRL. One who thinks he isn't.

FIRST GIRL (*after writing the answer*). A bigamist.

THIRD GIRL. One who makes the same mistake twice.

FIRST GIRL.   A co-ed.

FOURTH GIRL.   A girl who also goes to college.

FIRST GIRL.   A diplomat.

FIFTH GIRL.   A man who convinces his wife a woman looks fat in a fur coat.

FIRST GIRL.   An epitaph.

SIXTH GIRL.   A statement that lies above—about the one that lies below.

FIRST GIRL.   Flattery.

SEVENTH GIRL.   Perfume to be smelled of but not swallowed.

FIRST GIRL.   Hospital.

EIGHTH GIRL. A place where run-down people wind up.

FIRST GIRL.   Laundry.

SECOND GIRL.   A place where clothes are mangled.

FIRST GIRL.   Orator.

THIRD GIRL.   A chap who's always ready to lay down your life for his country.

FIRST GIRL.   A pessimist.

FOURTH GIRL.   One who of two evils chooses them both.

FIRST GIRL.   Resort.

FIFTH GIRL.   A place where the tired grow more tired.

FIRST GIRL.   Synonym.

SIXTH GIRL.   A word you use when you can't spell the other one.

FIRST GIRL.   A used car.

SEVENTH GIRL.   Not what it's jacked up to be.

FIRST GIRL.   Adult.

EIGHTH GIRL.   A person who has stopped growing at both ends and started growing in the middle.

FIRST GIRL.   Oh, thank you, girls.   I'll bet I get 100 on this.

A QUIZ FOR HIGH IQ'S

(The teacher is asking questions of his three best pupils, boys.)

TEACHER. Frank, what is a cannibal?

FIRST BOY. I don't know.

TEACHER. Oh, come now. If you ate your father and mother, what would you be?

FIRST BOY. Oh,—an orphan.

TEACHER. Mark, what is a hypocrite?

SECOND BOY. A kid that comes to school smiling.

TEACHER. Tommy, what animal is satisfied with the least nourishment?

THIRD BOY. That's easy. A moth, for it eats nothing but holes.

TEACHER. Why does the sun never set on the British flag, Frank?

FIRST BOY. Because they take it in at night.

TEACHER. Mark, what is the difference between lightning and electricity?

SECOND BOY. You don't have to pay for lightning.

TEACHER. Every day we breathe oxygen. What do we breathe at night, Tommy?

THIRD BOY. Nitrogen.

TEACHER. And now for our Bible lesson. What can you tell me about Aaron, Frank?

FIRST BOY. His name is first in the telephone book.

TEACHER. What do you think a land flowing with milk and honey would be like, Mark?

SECOND BOY. I think it would be sticky.

TEACHER. Tell me something about Good Friday, Tommy.

THIRD BOY. He was the chap that worked for Robinson Crusoe.

TEACHER. Frank, what does the story of Jonah and the whale teach us?

FIRST BOY. Er—er—you can't keep a good man down.

A QUIET EVENING AT HOME

(*Husband sits near a small radio. Wife is annoyed.*)

SHE. You think more of that silly old radio than you do of me.

HE. Well, I get less interference from it.

SHE. I think you're terrible. My first husband said I was far and away the best wife in the world.

HE. So you are, when you're far and away. And don't show me any more bills. I just can't face 'em.

SHE. But, dear, I don't want you to face them. I want you to foot them. And do get a new car. I've set my heart on a Cadillac.

HE. Well, that's the only part of your anatomy that'll ever sit on one.

SHE (*tearfully*). Arthur, do you love me still?

HE. Yes, better than any other way.

SHE. I made a speech at the Women's Club today. I was really outspoken.

HE. Who on earth outspoke you? By the way, I just read an article that says the cleverness of the father often proves a stumbling block to his son.

SHE. Well, thank goodness, our Bobby won't have anything to fall over.

(*He turns on the radio and she smiles sweetly.*)

MUSICAL NOTES

(Two women, old acquaintances, meet on the street and stop to talk.)

MRS. A. Hello, Mrs. Brown.

MRS. B. Hello, Mrs. Allen.

MRS. A. My daughter is having her voice trained. She'll be a singer.

MRS. B. Good. Is she improving?

MRS. A. Oh, yes. She used to be heard only three apartments away. Now we get complaints from the next building.

MRS. B. Bill Jones, that tenor cousin of mine, has a great voice. He can hold one of his notes for a whole minute.

MRS. A. That's nothing. My husband's held one of Bill's notes for two years.

MRS. B. He sings popular songs. That is, they were popular till he sings 'em.

MRS. A. I was going to be a singer myself but my teacher made me stop singing.

MRS. B. Why?

MRS. A. He said no matter whether he played on the white keys or the black keys, I always sang in the cracks. However, I'm still always breaking into song.

MRS. B. You wouldn't have to break in if you'd get the key. Good-bye.

MRS. A. Good-bye.

(They leave.)

YOU CAN'T PLEASE EVERYBODY

(*The scene is the lobby of a so-called hotel. Two men are talking*—MR. JONES, *the hotel proprietor and* MR. SMITH, *a dissatisfied guest.*)

SMITH. Look here, Jones, I've got a complaint to make about your hotel. The rain is pouring through the roof of my bedroom.

JONES. Of course, Mr. Smith. Don't we advertise running water in every room?

SMITH. Does the water always come through the roof like this?

JONES. Oh, no, sir. Only when it rains.

SMITH. Would you mind telling me with what material your beds are stuffed?

JONES. With straw, sir. The finest in the country.

SMITH. Well, now I know where the straw came from that broke the camel's back.

JONES. All our other guests seem to enjoy their stay with us, sir.

SMITH (*thoughtfully*). Well, the bed was too hard, your rates are too high, the food is terrible, there isn't any service and there is too much noise,—but I did like your ice water.

CHARITY BEGINS AT HOME

(*A* TRAMP *asks* MRS. STERN *for a handout.*)

HE. Madam, could you give a poor hungry chap a bite?

SHE. I don't bite myself, but I'll call the dog.

HE. Madam, I have seen better days.

SHE. So have I, but I've no time to talk about the weather with strangers. (*Gives him a penny.*) Here's a cent. How did you fall so low?

HE. Lady, I had your fault. I was too extravagant.

SHE. I remember your face. You are one of the tramps I gave a pie to last month.

HE. You are right, lady. You gave a pie to three of us. I am the sole survivor.

SHE (*angry*). Have you ever done a bit of work?

HE. Lady, if you think askin' dames like you for a handout ain't work, you don't know what work is.

SHE. Have you ever been offered work?

HE. Only once, lady, only once. Except for that I've met with nothing but kindness. (*Goes.*)

SHE. Lazy good-for-nothing!

Section Two
Stunts for All Occasions

NAME THE SONG

This stunt is a combination of charade and panto-mime. Answers may be given orally or written, but each contestant may have but one guess on a song. It is interesting to use both modern song titles and old-time ones. The following titles lend themselves to the game.

MODERN SONGS:

"Shake the Hand of a Stranger." Two people meet, pass, pause, turn around, shake hands, go on their way.

"I've Got the World on a String." Player crosses the stage, carrying on a string a large balloon on which is pasted a map of the world.

"Wish You Were Here." Man writes a postcard, looking very sad. Friend comes up and says, "How are you?" "Lonely," the man answers. "I miss Mary. I'm writing a card to tell her so. If she were here, I'd be having a fine time."

"Young and Foolish." A man and a woman watch some teenagers pass by, giggling, skipping, dancing, etc. Man says, "Where are they going?" Woman replies, "Goodness, how can I tell? They don't know themselves!" Man says, "I don't like it. They're too young and silly to be chasing around like that."

"Davy Crockett." Boy in Crockett costume meets another boy. They say, "Howdy, stranger." Davy says, "I'm a-goin' West. It's too crowded here."

"Turn Back the Hands of Time." Four people, each holding a clock, face the audience. Each turns the clock back, showing it first at correct time, then turning it back an hour or two.

"Stranger in Paradise." Put out signs saying, HEAVEN, CELESTIAL AVE., EDEN. Man enters,

looks about, shakes his head, reads the signs and is
more puzzled than before. Another man enters. First
man asks, "Is this the way to Cincinnati?" Second
one answers, "I don't know. I'm a stranger here myself."

"What Lola Wants Lola Gets." Lola sits alone.
Four other girls enter, each having something Lola
wants. All say, "Hello, Lola." Lola takes a library
book from the first girl, a bracelet from the second, a
box of candy from the third, and a pocketbook from
the fourth. They merely shake their heads in resignation and leave. Lola then walks off, smiling, with the
loot.

OLD SONGS:

"Alice, Where Are Thou?" Man enters, looks about,
calls loudly, "Alice, where are you?"

"Girl I Left Behind Me." A young couple walk on
stage, suddenly he darts off. She stands alone, weeps.
Another couple enters. They ask the weeping girl what
is the trouble. She sobs, "He went and left me." Boy
returns and says, "I knew I'd left something behind."

"Long, Long Ago." Two people hold out a long
strip of paper on which are printed either dates or
names of time long past, as The Flood, Battle of
Bunker Hill, 1492, 1066, etc.

"Oh, Dear, What Can the Matter Be?" Two women
are talking. First says, "It's time he was here. Maybe
he missed the bus." Second says, "He'd never miss the
bus." First, "It must be something serious." Second,
"Oh, dear! What can it be?"

"There's a Meeting Here Tonight." A small table
is covered with papers. Man says to the woman, "Keep
the children out of here tonight." The woman replies,
"They'll go to bed early. They know there's a meet-

ing."

"Where Has My Little Dog Gone?" Girl with a small toy dog enters, puts the dog on the floor, and says, "Stay here, Rover, till I come back." Boy enters as soon as the girl is gone, picks up the dog and runs off. Girl returns, calls, "Rover, where have you gone?"

"Come Where My Love Lies Dreaming." Girl lies on the rug asleep, as if asleep on grass. Boy looks at her smiling, calls to someone offstage. "Come here. She's asleep and dreaming."

"Smoke Gets in Your Eyes." A man smokes a cigarette and blows smoke toward a woman's face. She wipes her eyes and sniffles. He doesn't pay any attention but keeps on blowing smoke her way. She says, "I don't mind your smoking but the wind's blowing my way."

"The Lost Chord." A woman wraps up a large package, puts down the ball of cord, takes the package and rushes offstage. Man enters, sees the cord, says, "Just what I need," puts it in his pocket, and leaves. Woman returns, looks for the cord, and says, "Now where on earth can that cord be?"

PICK UP THE PAPER

Drop a rather small piece of crumpled paper on the floor. Have the contestant kneel about a foot from the paper, with arms folded across his chest. He bends his head and trunk forward and picks up the paper in his mouth without falling flat on his face, if possible.

WHO AM I?

Each player selects a well-known Bible character. Then, in one sentence, the player gives a clue to his or her identity, and the audience guesses who is represented. The person wins who identifies the greatest number correctly. No one player is allowed more than one guess as to any one character. Suggested characters to be used and sentences:

I built a famous sea-going vessel—**Noah**

It took me thirteen years to build my house of stone and cedar—**Solomon**

I drove a chariot and exceeded the speed limit—**Jehu**

I was hanged on the gallows I had prepared for another—**Haman**

I had very bad luck but was always patient—**Job**

I played well on a stringed instrument—**David**

I was an Egyptian ruler who pursued the children of Israel with horses and chariots—**Pharaoh**

I was a prophetess and Aaron's sister—**Miriam**

I was the father-in-law of Moses—**Jethro**

I was not a barber but I shaved a great man's head—**Delilah**

I was the great champion of the Philistines—**Goliath**

I made a fiery serpent and placed it on a pole—**Moses**

Saul consulted me once because of my magic powers—**The Witch of Endor**

I had a very salty wife—**Lot**

I was Isaac's youngest son and I dreamed of a ladder—**Jacob**

I was Jacob's oldest son—**Reuben**

I was one woman who never quarreled with her mother-in-law—**Ruth**

I am the queen who made King Ahasuerus angry

because I refused his invitation to a party—**Vashti**

I am a short man who climbed a tall tree—**Zacchaeus**

I did many good deeds in Joppa and when I died Peter brought me back to life—**Dorcas**

BOOK TITLES—
AS THEY MIGHT HAVE BEEN

The leader gives the title and the one who knows the answer raises his hand. Someone keeps the score and at the end of the game the individual having the most correct answers is the winner. Other titles may be added to those suggested.

Blown Away—**Gone With the Wind**

The Ancient Store for the Inquisitive—**Old Curiosity Shop**

My Relative's Home—**Uncle Tom's Cabin**

Those Way Up and Very Important—**The High and the Mighty**

That Man from the South, Sir—**The Virginian**

The Plain of Corncakes—**Tortilla Flat**

It's Not as if I Didn't Know Him—**Not as a Stranger**

Affection Lasts Forever—**Love is Eternal**

She Wears a Red Letter on Her Sweater—**The Scarlet Letter**

Riches Surrounded by Water—**Treasure Island**

A Story About Two Big Places—**A Tale of Two Cities**

I Won't Weep Today—**I'll Cry Tomorrow**

Ocean Everywhere—**The Sea Around Us**

From Now Right On Forever—**From Here to Eternity**

Hi, Ivan, Go Work in the Garden—**Ivanhoe**

AN I.Q. TEST

The leader puts the players in a circle and announces he will call on one whose hand is raised first. His assistant has the names of the players and puts a check by the name when that person answers correctly. A mistake scores a zero and a zero cancels a correct answer. The winner is hailed as having the highest I.Q. in the group. Suggested questions:

Who was the most patient man known? **Job**

Name three mountains mentioned in the Bible. **Ararat, Gilead, Zion**

Who in the Bible was known as The Preacher? **Ecclesiastes**

What Biblical character was noted for his wisdom? **Solomon**

Of what country was Cymbeline, the Shakespearean character, king? **Britain**

Of what land was Pericles, another character from Shakespeare, a native? **Tyre**

Name King Lear's three daughters. **Goneril, Regan, Cordelia**

Who wrote Little Dorrit? **Dickens**

What is probably the most famous dream in literature? **Midsummer Night's Dream**

Name the most famous lovers in literature. **Romeo and Juliet**

What man never had to take sleeping pills? **Rip van Winkle**

What famous traveler in fiction met the strangest people? **Gulliver**

Who wrote Paradise Lost? **Milton**

If wishes were horses, what would beggars do? **Ride**

Name a famous bow and arrow man. **William Tell**

In what famous play was the pirate Captain Hook?
Peter Pan

Give the next line of this poem and name the author:
"Tell me not in mournful numbers—Life is but an
empty dream." **Longfellow**

Name three well-known songs with a girl's name in
the title. **Annie Laurie, Sweet Evelina, Sally in Our
Alley**

Name three well known songs with a man's name in
the title. **Ben Bolt, Dan Tucker, John Peel**

Name a large city in each of these countries: Japan,
Brazil, Portugal, Australia, Norway. **Tokyo, Rio de
Janeiro, Lisbon, Melbourne, Oslo**

MAKE YOUR MARK

For this you need a piece of red chalk and a strong
mop handle. Place a mat on the floor. The contestant
takes one end of the mop handle firmly in both hands
and holds the piece of chalk in one hand at the same
time. He puts the end of the mop handle not in his
hands about four feet in front of his own feet. Then
he leans over with his entire weight on the mop handle
and makes a chalk mark on the floor as far as he can
reach. No part of his body may touch the floor except
of course his feet. If it is a contest, the one making
the mark farthest from his toes wins.

MISSING WORD

Fill in the missing word in the hymn title. Answers may be oral or written. Person with the poorest score must be made to sing a verse of one of the hymns.

As (Pants) the Hart for Cooling Streams
Jerusalem the (Golden)
When I (Survey) the Wondrous Cross
In Royal (David's) City
A Mighty (Fortress) is Our God
O, Come All Ye (Faithful)
Hark the (Herald) Angels Sing
The Holy (City)
Away in a (Manger)
Eternal Father Strong to (Save)
Work for the (Night) is Coming
Comfort Ye My (People)
Go Tell it in the (Mountain)
Oh, Lord (Most) Holy
If With All Your (Hearts)

REGISTERING EMOTIONS

The players are in a line facing the judge who will, at the end of the stunt, award a medal, made of cardboard with a horrible face drawn on it, to the contestant who best registers the required emotion.

Emotions may be: sorrow, joy, hate, horror, embarrassment, fear, surprise, stupidity, amnesia, sleepiness, annoyance, anger, pain, hunger, thirst, dizziness, etc.

BIBLE HISTORY TEST

Have players in two teams and a tester and a timer. The tester asks the questions. The timer sees that no more than one minute is taken for each question and answer. The tester begins with the first person in team one, then goes to the first person in team two, and so on. Any contestant giving a wrong answer or no answer is out. The team with the most survivors at the end of the test wins.

QUESTIONS:

How wide is a handbreadth? **The width of a man's four fingers laid out flat or a little more than 3½ inches**

What is the modern name of a leviathan? **Crocodile**

Name the ten plagues. **Water made blood, Frogs, Lice, Flies, Murrain, Boils and Blains, Thunder and Hail, Locusts, Darkness, Death of the First Born**

How many horns has a unicorn? **One**

Who smote a rock and made water come out so the thirsty might drink? **Moses**

Were the sons of Anak dwarfs or giants or neither? **Giants**

From what city did Samson remove the gates? **Geza**

How long is a cubit? **The measure of a man's arm from the elbow to the end of the middle finger**

Who was Jonathan's father? **Saul**

What queen came to test Solomon's intelligence? **Sheba**

Who was cured of leprosy by washing in the Jordan River seven times? **Naaman**

Complete this proverb. The wicked flee—**when no man pursueth**

Name a city in which David dwelt that has the same name as a character in the play, The Tempest. **Ariel**

What prophet's name is given to a tale of sorrow or disappointment? **Jeremiah's name—jeremiad**

What prophet saw wheels and cherubim in a vision? **Ezekiel**

Name two Biblical kings each of whose names contain the letter z twice: **Belshazzar, Nebuchadnezzar**

Who was the wife of Ananias? **Sapphira**

Most of the apostles followed what occupation? **Fishing**

What do the words Alpha and Omega mean? **Beginning. End**

Complete this proverb: A time to weep and a time to laugh, a time to mourn and—**a time to dance**

AIN'T IT?

The leader asks each player a question and the one-word answer must rhyme with ain't. If player fails to give such an answer he is out of the game. The leader explains first and then makes the questions as puzzling or difficult as possible.

Is this your best dress? **'Tain't**

What sort of music do you prefer? **Faint**

What is your hobby? **Paint**

Have you a good disposition? **Quaint**

What was your last letter about? **Plaint or complaint**

Did he really do that work or just pretend? **Feint**

When "aint's" run out switch to words that rhyme with is, ate, etc.

TRUE OR FALSE

Players stand or sit in a line. There is a questioner and a judge. If a correct answer is given, the Judge claps his hands. If the answer is wrong, the Judge rings a bell and the answerer is out of the game. The winner is one who makes no mistakes. If desired, the players may be in two teams, answering alternately. The following statements will do for starters:

There must have been a television set on the island since there was an Ariel in the play called The Tempest. **False**

Cleopatra killed herself by taking too many headache pills. **False**

A bittern is a bird of the heron type. **True**

Aaron's rod was a fishing pole. **False**

Samson carried off the gates of Geza. **True**

The widow's cruise, mentioned in the Bible, was on the Red Sea. **False**

A satyr is a person who sits all day. **False**

Mary's little lamb made the children cry. **False**

Barley, corn, and rye are foods. **True**

A sinatra is a musical composition. **False**

Three wise men of Gotham went to sea in a bowl. **True**

In Mother Goose blackbirds were baked into a pie. **True**

Gopher wood is wood saw into planks by gophers. **False**

Kangaroos and frogs both live in water. **False**

Martha Washington was a widow when she married George Washington. **True**

SHAKESPEARE'S PLAYS

Charades in which answers are each the title of a play by Shakespeare.

"Two Gentlemen of Verona." Two men cross the stage, each carrying a suitcase on sides of which are large posters bearing the name, Verona.

"The Tempest." Put a pile of loose papers on the floor. At the back of screen rattle a sheet of tin to give the sound of a storm. Turn on an electric fan from back of screen and blow papers about.

"Merry Wives of Windsor." Any number of women with market baskets walk across the stage. They stop in center to talk. First: "It's too bad they won't deliver out to Windsor." Second: "Oh, well, it's fun to go to market." Third and Fourth: "Let's be cheerful." All laugh loudly and leave.

"King Lear." Man smiles at any number of passing women. One says, "Hello, Mr. King. That's a sweet smile." Man replies, "That's no smile—that's a leer."

"Measure for Measure." One girl has a yard stick, another a tape measure. They meet, hold out the articles, and exchange them.

"Twelfth Night." Two women are talking. First, "How's Bob?" Second, "Very sick. He's worse at night." First, "How long has he been ill?" Second, "A week and five days today. I dread tonight."

"The Merchant of Venice." Man has a large basket filled with junk. He crosses the stage calling, "All the latest gadgets from Venice. Cheap. Come buy. All the latest gadgets from Venice."

"The Winter's Tale." Player reads aloud from a book: "It was a stormy snowy night in January. Snow and ice covered everything and traveling was impossible. This strange story begins when two weary wanderers asking for a night's lodging at the little country inn where icicles were a yard long.

"**As You Like It.**" A man and his wife are talking. She, "How do you want your steak, dear? Well done?" He, "No." She, "Rare?" He, "No." She, "Medium?" He, "No." She, "Well, I want to please you, dear. How *would* you like it?"

"**Midsummer Night's Dream.**" Two girls are talking. First, "I had a wonderful dream last night. And I never dreamed before." Second, "Last night was the middle of summer. Folks always dream then my grandmother says."

MIXED UP LETTERS

Have cards or sheets of paper on which are printed, in large letters, scrambled words. This may be a written game. If oral, have two teams, members of which take turns in answering. If one fails, the next person in the second team tries to answer. Those who fail must sit down. The team having the most standees at the end of the game wins. Have a brief time limit for thinking of answers. Words:

subdra—absurd	eonhts—honest
ttaabnl—blatant	neasni—insane
burche—cherub	jkneir—jerkin
dtnlae—dental	nneelk—kennel
orceen—encore	llbaai—labial
eautfc—faucet	lareimn—mineral
rednef—fender	wynse—newsy
htrgea—gather	eernv—nerve or never

WHAT'S IN THE ANT HILL?

Answers may be oral or written. The one with the most correct answers wins the prize. If answers are oral give each one who answers a question correctly, a grain of dried corn or popcorn. The one who has the most grains at the end is the winner. Repeat the question only once if oral. If written, have a definite time limit in which the papers are to be finished.

This ant is an enemy. **ANTagonist**

In the south but not a hot ant.   **ANTarctic**
This ant is connected with a stake.   **ANTe**
This ant has a long tongue.   **ANTeater**
This ant goes before in history.   **ANTedate**
This ant is very graceful.   **ANTelope**
This ant is on every roof.   **ANTenna**
This ant is a place where you wait.   **ANTeroom**
This ant is a song of praise.   **ANThem**
This ant is part of a seed plant.   **ANTher**
This ant is a group of islands.   **ANTilles**
This ant is a disease of cattle.   **ANThrax**
An ant that resembles man.   **ANThropoid**
A caper.   **ANTic**
This ant likes to expect things.   **ANTicipate**
A remedy for poison.   **ANTidote**
A direct opposite.   **ANTipodes**
He likes old things.   **ANTiquary**
Ask the deer about this one.   **ANTler**
A famous character in a play by Shakespeare. **ANTonio**

WHO'S ZOO?

This is an oral game. The leader defines the animal and calls on any player. One failing to answer correctly is out. Winners are those who stay in to the finish.

This one has a long neck—**Giraffe**
Most industrious creature—**Ant**
Has fondest embrace—**Bear**
Is taken fishing—**Worm**
Will sit and muse about things—**Cat**
Needs medicine for his throat—**Horse**
You'd better not cross it—**Lion** (**line**)
A copy-cat—**Ape**
He loves to follow your steps—**Dog**
You are sometimes it—**Goat**
A greedy creature—**Pig**
Goes astray, as do we all—**Sheep**
Held in affection—**Deer**
Has a built-in nursery—**Kangaroo**
You really hadn't—**Otter**
He kept on the mark—**Toad**
He can cry loudly—**Whale**
This one may overawe you—**Cow**
Loves to fool with things—**Monkey**
Has a trunk and can trumpet—**Elephant**
A meek little thing—**Mouse**
He will shrink in terror—**Quail**
Reminds me of folks who repeat everything they hear—**Parrot**
Used by little league players—**Bat**
Good in numbers—**Rabbit**

WHO WAS WHO?

Players are required to name two people whose names begin with the same letter and tell why they are famous. The beginner starts with the letter A; the next player uses the letter B and so on down the alphabet. If there are not twenty-six players, some will have to use two different letters. Here are some names that might be used:

A. George Ade, an American humorist
   Aesop, a Greek writer of fables
B. Balboa, a Spanish explorer
   P. T. Barnum, an American showman
C. Al Capone, an American gangster
   Benvenuto Cellini, Italian goldsmith
D. Daniel Defoe, English novelist
   Eleanora Duse, Italian actress
E. Sir Edward Elgar, English composer
   Euclid, Greek mathematician
F. Henry Ford, American industrialist
   Sigmund Freud, Austrian psychoanalyst
G. Mahatma Gandhi, Hindu leader
   Lou Gehrig, American baseball player
H. Frans Hals, a Dutch painter
   Hannibal, a Carthaginian general
I. Washington Irving, an American author
   George Innes, an American painter
J. Jesse James, an American outlaw
   Louis Jolliet, a Canadian explorer
K. John Keats, an English poet
   William Kidd, a pirate from Scotland
L. Charles Lamb, an English essayist
   LaSalle, a French explorer
M. Niccolo Machiavelli, an Italian political philosopher

Nellie Melba, an Australian soprano
N. Carrie Nation, an American temperance leader
Horatio Nelson, a British naval officer
O. Omar (Khayyam), a Persian poet
Ovid, a Roman poet
P. Anna Pavlova, a Russian dancer
Pocahontas, an American Indian princess
Q. Josiah Quincy, an American orator and patriot
Marcus Quintilian, a Roman critic
R. Rasputin, a Russian monk
Maurice Revel, a French composer
S. Thomas Sheraton, an English furniture designer.

John L. Sullivan, an American boxer
T. Mark Twain, an American humorist
Titian, an Italian painter
U. Urban, the name of eight popes
Ulpian, a Roman jurist
V. Anthony Van Dyck, a Flemish painter
Guiseppi Verdi, an Italian composer
W. David Warfield, an American actor
John Wesley, an English religious leader
X. Xenephon, a Greek historian and general
Xerxes, a king of Persia
Y. Charlotte Yonge, an English novelist
Brigham Young, an American Mormon leader
Z. Zoroaster, the founder of an ancient Persian religion
Zola, a French novelist.

WHAT FIGURES!

Ask a contestant to make a figure 8 in the air with his toe and a figure 6 with his finger.

WHAT GROUNDS?

One player tells the others he is going to sue someone and when they ask him why he gives the reason and they give him advice.

Player. "I'm suing my wife for divorce."

Others. "On what grounds?" (Usually one person will reply.)

Player. "I came home and found my wife flirting with a man who owes me money."

Others. "He was probably just paying her a little interest."

Second Player. "My wife got a divorce yesterday."

Others. "Why? Incompatibility?"

Second Player. "No. Just the first two syllables, in come."

Third Player. "Mrs. Smith, why are you getting married again? You've had three husbands and they all went crazy or something."

Mrs. Smith. "I know, but I want a safe and a sane fourth."

Fourth Player. "Mr. Jones, why do you want a divorce from your wife? Aren't your relations pleasant?"

Mr. Jones. "Mine are. Hers are terrible."

Fifth Player. "I'm getting a divorce from my wife."

Sixth Player. "On what grounds?"

Fifth Player. "Coffee grounds. My cup's always full of 'em."

Seventh Player. "Well, I'm suing my mother-in-law."

Eighth Player. "Why? On what grounds?"

Seventh Player. "Because my dog bit her and now he's sick. I'd throw her out of the window but I'm afraid she might fall on somebody and hurt 'em."

Ninth Player. "I'm going to sue an efficiency expert who charged me $50 for his course."

Tenth Player. "On what grounds?"

Ninth Player. "He said he'd show me how to earn more money than I'm getting and I've been doing that for years."

This may be varied to suit the crowd. The sillier the suits and the reasons the better.

LIGHT REFRESHMENTS

Each player gets the name of one of the following articles of food pinned on his or her back. It is printed on a sheet of white paper. No player knows what is on his back but nevertheless must try to find his partner. He may ask any of the other players five questions about himself. If, after this, he does not find his partner he is out of the game. The one who first guesses his own identity and finds his partner wins. For example the one marked BREAD might ask "Am I dessert?" The answer will be "No." "Am I eaten hot or cold?" The answer is "Both." Etc. Suggested combinations: Bread and butter, Ham and eggs, Cakes and ale, Pork and beans, Tea and crumpets, pancakes and sausage, ice cream and cake, toast and tea, peas and carrots, doughnuts and coffee, waffles and honey, cornflakes and bananas, peaches and cream, hot dogs and mustard, fish and chips, corn and beans, toast and marmalade, etc.

BLACK OUT

The players are told that the leader will ask them questions which are to be answered with one word only, the name of a color. If the one questioned answers "Black" the Leader says "Out," without explaining, and the one who said "Black" leaves the game. It usually takes quite a few minutes before the players realize that "Black" is the forbidden word. Questions should be varied but not too difficult. For example:

What sea has the name of a color? **Red Sea**
What sort of study shows deep thinking? **Brown**
What mountains have the name of a color? **Green**
What color shows a depressed state of mind? **Blue**
What color are storm clouds? **Gray or black**
According to a well-known rhyme you never saw a cow this color. **Purple**
A cowardly color. **Yellow**
If you're in this color, you're feeling fine. **Pink**
This color belongs with old lace. **Lavender**
The name of a fruit. **Orange**
The kind of mark no student wants. **Black**
A flag of truce is this color. **White**
Part of a famous pirate's name. **Black (Blackbeard)**
Rabbits like food this color. **Green**
A kind of dog. **Gray (Grayhound)**
A small prevarication. **White (Little white lie)**
A kind of card game begins with this. **Black (black-jack)**

And so on. Have many questions that are answered by the color black.

SEE WHAT I MEAN?

This is a guessing game about seas or oceans. The clue is a very short pantomime, the pantomimists having chosen subjects themselves.

1.   One player, with a toy telephone, tries to get a number. She listens but there is no dial tone. She shakes head despairingly and gives up. **Dead Sea.**

2.   Player picks up a book, turns the pages rapidly, and puts the book down. **Red Sea.**

3.   Player looks at samples of colored cloth, and selects the black. **Black Sea.**

4.   Player shivers, shakes, teeth chatter. **Arctic Sea.**

5.   Two players enter and appear to quarrel violently. A third enters and calms them down. They go off arm in arm. **Pacific Ocean.**

6.   Boy enters, pantomimes shooting with a bow and arrow, gives a warwhoop (silently). **Indian Ocean.**

7.   Player looks at a compass, keeps pointing to the north and walks off in that direction. **North Sea.**

8.   Player audibly buzzes like a bee, flies about the stage, stops and twists a ring on his finger. **Behring Sea. Bee-ring.**

9.   Player puts down on a table a tray on which there are fancy cups and saucers. **China Sea.**

10.   Player sings, whistles or hums, audibly, a well-known Irish tune, "Killarney," "Come Back to Erin," etc. **Irish Sea.**

The contestant who names most seas correctly first wins the prize, a map or a pair of sun glasses.

TALL STORIES

Six players sit before the audience and the announcer says: "These people have had great adventures and will each tell you about one of their unusual experiences." The six then tell crazy and incredible stories. For example:

First. I have a very intelligent puppy. One night my house got on fire. We all rushed out and everyone was safe, but Rover turned back and ran into the house. Soon he came back, scorched and panting, carrying, what do you think? My fire insurance policy wrapped in a wet towel.

Second. Talk about rapid building! In my home town they lay the foundation stone of an apartment house on Monday and on Friday they're putting tenants out for back rent.

Third. In my state we have the biggest mosquitoes in the world. One night I got a candle and went around burning them but one big fellow just turned around and blew out the candle.

Fourth. Have you ever seen the Natural Bridge in Virginia? Well, my father built it.

Fifth. Of course elephants remember. When I was a boy I once gave a circus elephant a stick of striped candy. After that whenever that same circus paraded in town the barbers had to take in their striped poles. The elephant thought they were peppermint sticks.

Sixth. You folks here don't know what cold weather is. When I was up at the Arctic Circle the candles froze and we couldn't blow them out. When we talked the words came out of our mouths in chunks of ice and we had to fry them to see what we were talking about.

A prize might be given to the tallest story as selected by the listeners.

BE AN ANIMAL

Players each select a different animal to imitate.
Each comes out and does his or her stunt while the
audience guess what animal is represented. Give a prize
for the best portrayal. Here are some suggestions:

Duck. Spread feet apart slightly, squat down, reach
between legs and grasp heels, thumbs in and hands
crossed. Lean forward and waddle across the room.

Elephant. Two boys face each other. First boy
puts his hands on the second's shoulders, jumps up and
locks legs about him, body near his shoulders. Second
boy stands with his feet apart. First boy lets arms and
body hang down in back, swings his hands and head
between the other's legs and grabs him firmly by the
heels. The second boy now falls straight forward on
his hands, and walks forward on his hands and feet, the
first boy assisting him by lifting his feet by the ankles
he is holding.

Seal. Actor bends down to the floor, places his hands
on the floor and extends his body straight backward,
resting on his hands and toes. This makes a straight
line from the shoulders to his heels. He pushes on his
hands abruptly, throwing his body up from the floor,
claps his hands together, sways his head from side to
side, replaces his hands at the side. He may try to
clap his hands and feet at the same time.

Camel. Two boys stand close, facing the same way.
The one in front, helped by his partner, jumps up backward and locks his legs under the other's arms. He
then lowers his body between the other's legs and grasps
his ankles. First one lowers himself down, resting on
his hands. He then walks forward on his hands and
feet, swaying and lurching. The other lifts his part-

ner's legs by the ankles at each step. One boy may do this alone, putting his feet far apart, bending over, his hands flat on the floor in front of him, his knees and elbows straight and stiff. He walks forward, the hand and leg on same side moving together.

Frog. This may be a race between two frogs. Boy squats down, his hands flat on the floor about two feet before his feet. The knees must not touch the floor. From all fours the frog leaps forward for a short distance, landing on his hands. He then moves his feet forward, near but outside the hands. He remains in a squat position, his hands on the floor.

Lobster. Boy bends his knees and puts his hands on the floor behind him, then back to the floor, his elbows straight and stiff. He moves backward. Only his hands and feet should touch the ground.

Worm. Player puts his hands on the floor and jumps with his feet backward so a straight line is formed from shoulders to heels. Then, with his hands in place, his elbows rigid, he walks short steps up to his hands. Then, feet still, he walks on his hands a short distance. He alternates the feet and hand walk until he crosses the room.

Caterpillar. This takes two boys. They face the same way, the one behind jumps on the other's back, his legs locked about his thighs. The front one bends over and rests his hands on the floor. The sitter does the same thing over the head of the front one. Now both are resting their hands on the floor. They walk around, the same hand of both moving at same time. Knees are stiff.

Donkey. Player stands on his right foot, the trunk bent forward, his left leg stretched straight back. He leaps off the right foot, stretching it backward and bringing the left foot forward under the trunk which must remain horizontal. Do this step in rhythm for twenty or more counts, then give a loud bray and sink to the floor exhausted.

WHAT'S IN THE BEE HIVE?

The answer to each question is a word beginning with the syllable **be.** The question is read but once. One answering first wins a point. One with the most points at the end of the game wins. May be written with a strict time limit for writing the answers.

Shore—**BEach**
Watchtower—**BEacon**
Mace bearer—**BEedle**
One of man's best friends—**BEagle**
A wide-mouthed drinking cup—**BEaker**
To defy—**BEard**
A lady in Much Ado About Nothing—**BEatrice**
To cloud—**BEdim**
A heavy ramming instrument—**BEetle**
To confuse—**BEfuddle**
Flowering plant—**BEgonia**
To delude by craft—**BEguile**
An East Indian lady of rank—**BEgum**
A command—**BEhest**
What mothers do to naughty children—**BErate**
Supplicate—**BEseech**
To beleaguer—**BEsiege**
To confuse—**BEwilder**
Away out yonder—**BEyond**
An old card game—**BEzique**

ROW YOUR BOAT

There are two teams, eight in each. They sit cross-legged on the floor as if in a boat. The leader tells them they are about to take part in a boat race but of course they have to have oars. He shows them large oars or paddle-shaped pieces of cardboard, or even stiff paper folded like an oar. He says each member of the team must earn his oar by answering a question correctly. All questions will be about oars. If a question is answered incorrectly someone else gets a chance, someone on the other team. When asked the question those who think they know the answer raise a hand. The one who raises a hand first is called on. The team that earns all its oars first bends forward and, in pantomime, rows away rapidly. Here are some appropriate questions:

An oar for the birds—**Ornithology**

An oar for your feet—**Orthopedic**

An oar that is spoken—**Oral**

A musical oar—**Oratorio**

An oar that gives wise answers—**Oracle**

This one makes elaborate speeches—**Orator**

This one chases itself, it goes round and round. **Orbit**

An oar that is a fruit—**Orange**

A huge animal—**Orang-outan**

An oar hard to bear—**Ordeal**

This one commands—**Order**

A commonplace oar—**Ordinary**

An oar made of fine cloth—**Organdy**

Put this in your house to look out of—**Oriel**

This is a bird—**Oriole**

An oar that is a prayer—**Orison**

An eastern oar—**Orient**

A kind of antelope—**Oryx**
This oar is sound in doctrine—**Orthodox**
An oar that deals with spelling and writing—**Orthography**
One with a strong clear voice—**Orotund**
One without parents—**Orphan**
The lowest deck of a sailing vessel—**Orlop**
A decoration—**Ornament**
A musical instrument—**Organ**

HE ALWAYS GETS HIS MAN

Players stand in a circle. Each player draws a paper from a hat which is passed around. All papers are blank but one on which is the word, MURDERER. The one who draws this paper is told to leave the room. Slips are collected and F.B.I. is written on one. They are put back in the hat and again drawn by the players. Everyone but the murderer knows who is the F.B.I. man. The murderer is called back and told to murder someone but not to get caught. Players in the circle turn about so their backs are toward the center. The murderer enters the circle not knowing there is an F.B.I. man in it. He makes believe to stab one of the players who falls to the floor, dead. The murderer coughs loudly and all turn around toward him. The F.B.I. man tries to catch him but the murderer must get out of the circle before he is touched. Most players try to assist the F.B.I. man though some side with the murderer.

WHAT DO YOU THINK YOU ARE?

Have the players see who can tell the right answer first.

A card game—something the dentist makes—something to cross over. **Bridge**

A small opening—a heavy rainstorm—a deep study. **Pour—pore**

A glance—a popular magazine—expectation. **Look**

An animal—a stockmarket term—a blunder—a papal letter. **Bull**

A domestic animal—a stupid fellow—a small engine. **Donkey**

An ancient German people—candid—exempt. **Frank**

A playing card—a man's name—a contrivance to turn a spit. **Jack**

To wedge in—something to eat—the side of a doorway. **Jamb—jam**

A reward—to interfere—tamper. **Medal—meddle**

Uncommon—underdone—not dense. **Rare**

SEND A TELEGRAM

Write ten words beginning with letters in a ten-letter given word, in the proper order. Allow a short time for the writing of the message after paper and pencils are passed and word is told. Give prize for the funniest or most sensible message. Give a word like: Presenting. The telegram might read: "Pick ripe elevators shelling each, never touching insides nor gravy." Or it might say: "Please return Emma's silver epergne—need to introduce new goulash."

MY GREATEST ACHIEVEMENT

Each player is called on to tell in one sentence his greatest achievement. He, of course, says something very silly. The one whose achievement is considered by the audience the funniest or the most improbable wins the prize, which might appropriately be a book of tales. If desired, achievements may be written on cards before the game and contestants each draw a card, reading what is on it when called on. Here are some achievements:

I rubbed two boy scouts together and made a fire.

I went through High School and never learned a thing.

I raced with a snail and was beaten by only two lengths, lengths of me, not the snail.

I never lose my presence of mind because I have no mind.

I am a very popular boy with the girls who all say I am their favorite boy not to go out with.

My greatest achievement is that I never lose my vim and vigor, because I always rest before I get tired.

I am a wonderful dancer for I never step on my partner's feet, only on my own.

I am an expert stenographer, for it took Gray seven years to write his *Elegy in a Country Churchyard*, and I did it in seven minutes.

I did so well in my final college exams I was second from the top in the list of those who failed.

I am probably the most skilled mathematician in the world for I can add a long row of figures ten times and get ten different answers.

I worked my way up from the bottom—from a bootblack to a hairdresser.

I taught my baby sister to behave at her christening for I practiced with her a whole week using a watering pot.

My greatest achievement is getting along with my wife; in the morning she does what she wants and in the afternoon I do what she wants.

My greatest achievement was opening a joint bank account with my husband—a deposit account for him and a checking account for me.

I found a quarter yesterday after the last horse race so I didn't have to walk home.

INITIALS

The leader holds up a large card on which are shown the initials of a famous person. Whoever guesses the person first scores a point. When all cards have been displayed points are counted to see who wins. Suggested initials are:

T.A.E.—Thomas A. Edison
H.B.S.—Harriet Beecher Stowe
H.S.T.—Harry S. Truman
D.D.E.—Dwight D. Eisenhower
M.W.—Martha Washington
R.R.H.—Red Riding Hood
B.B.—Bernard Baruch
S.C.—Santa Claus
E.B.B.—Elizabeth Barrett Browning
C.B.L.—Claire Booth Luce
S.C.—Sebastian Cabot
M.T.—Mark Twain

TAKE YOUR CHOICE

Each guest is offered a choice; he must do one of two things suggested by the leader or pay a fine, the money in the fine box to go to charity. Here are some things a victim might be asked to choose from:

1. Stand on your head or guess what countries are represented by the following pantomimes: a—girl stands shivering, rubbing hands together. **Chile**—chilly. b—girl looking with disgust at a handkerchief covered with gravy spots. **Greece**—grease. c—boy flapping arms like wings, stretching up neck and moving lips as if saying gobble. **Turkey**

2. Turn three somersaults without stopping or name three or more very small fictional characters—**Tiny (Tim), Wee (Willie Winkie), Little (Boy Blue or Bopeep) Baby (Bunting)**, etc.

3. Eat three soda crackers and immediately whistle How Dry I Am, or name two famous authors whose names are used in exclamations—**Scott** (Great Scott!), **Dickens** (The Dickens!)

4. Recite the twelve times multiplication table backwards rapidly without pause or mistake, or answer these two questions—Whose elephants crossed the Alps? (**Hannibal's.**) Who crossed the Rubicon? (**Caesar.**)

5. Take any guest who volunteers and give him a piggy-back ride, or answer these questions correctly: Which of these languages is spoken natively by the most people, English, Chinese, or Russian? (**Chinese.**) Where was the first European university? (**Salerno, Italy, a school of medicine.**)

6. Sit in the corner and do not move or speak for the next half hour or name three very famous waterfalls and their location. For example, these might be given: **Niagara—New York and Canada, Victoria—Southern**

Rhodesia, Shoshone—Idaho.

7. Run around a circle backward three times without stopping or name the three longest rivers in the world. Rivers are **Nile, Missouri-Mississippi, Amazon.**

8. Roll a peanut across the room with your nose, hands behind your back, or name three Nobel prize winners all of whom are United States authors. **Sinclair Lewis, Pearl Buck, Eugene O'Neill.**

9. Sing one verse and the chorus of any song chosen by the audience or name the seven wonders of the world. These are: **Pyramids of Egypt, Hanging Gardens of Babylon, Statue of Zeus (Jupiter) at Olympia, Temple of Artemis (Diana) at Ephesus, Mausoleum at Halicarnassus, Colossus at Rhodes, Pharos (lighthouse) of Alexandria.**

10. Stand, bend backward, and touch the floor with your hands, or name the four largest oceans in the world in order of area. **Pacific, Atlantic, Indian, Arctic.**

WHO KNOWS WHOSE NOSE

This is extremely silly but very amusing. There are two groups with a leader for each. The leader puts the cover of a match box on his nose. Judge cries GO. Each leader then turns to his next in line and tries, not using his hands, to get the free end of the match box cover off his nose and on the nose of his neighbor. The group getting the cover to the last nose first wins. If the cover falls, it must be taken back to the leader and he must start all over again.

WHAT'S MY LINE?

NEW EDITION

A player tells one thing about his or her line and others guess what it is. The one who guesses correctly first then gives the hint as to his line, and so on until all have taken part. For example:

A housewife uses my line—**Clothes line**
Isaac Walton used my line—**Fish line**
I'm good for speedy travel—**Airline**
I'm in a song—**(Sweet) Adeline**
I'm rather salty—**Saline**
Sailors use me—**Bow line**
I prefer a recumbent position—**Recline**
I help move vessels—**Tow line**
I am a graceful animal—**Feline**
I have an evil disposition—**Malign**

DON'T ASK ME

One person, the Asker, is sent out of the room. The others decide which of their number is to be the Answerer. The Asker is then called in and may ask any question he wishes but it will be answered only by the Answerer. Anyone else on whom he calls replies, "Don't ask me." If he calls on a wrong person six times he must pay a forfeit and another Asker is chosen. If he calls on the right person in six tries or less he wins a prize and the right person called on becomes the Asker.

COMPLETE THESE PHRASES

The announcer gives a partial phrase to the competitors and calls on the one who raises his hand first. The one who gives a wrong answer is out. Each player who gives the right answer takes a penny from the plate on the table. The one having the most pennies at the end of the game wins. She is then told the pennies must be put on the collection plate next Sunday. Phrases— to which many others may be added:

Gog and	(Magog)
Dan to	(Beersheba)
David and	(Goliath)
Balm of	(Gilhead)
Forest of	(Lebanon)
Rose of	(Sharon)
House of	(Rimmon)
The priests and the	(Levites)
The gold of	(Ophir)
Depart from	(evil)
More precious than	(rubies)
Ships of	(Tarshish)
A lion is in	(the streets)
My brother's	(keeper)
Quit yourselves like	(men)
A still small	(voice)
The noise of many	(waters)
The little foxes that spoil	(the vines)
A living dog is better than a	(dead lion)
A land flowing with	(milk and honey)
A proverb and a	(byword)
Wisdom shall	(die with you)

Wisdom is better than   (rubies)
New wine into old   (bottles)
Thirty pieces of   (silver)

WHAT'S MY CRIME?
OR
WHO AM I?

Answers may be oral or written. If oral, only one answer may be given to a question. If written, have a time limit.

I couldn't stand having a woman in the house. **Bluebeard**

I liked gold harps and hens and money. **Jack, the Giant Killer**

I was a king who didn't care much for children. **Herod**

I loved to play the fiddle by a nice hot fire. **Nero**

Daughter of a king and wife of a king I introduced the worship of Baal. **Jezebel**

I was a dancer who liked a good head rather than a good hand when I finished. **Salome**

I washed my hands but couldn't get the stain off. **Lady Macbeth**

A woman with a "familiar spirit," visited by Saul. **Witch of Endor**

I killed a bear when I was very young. **Davy Crockett**

After a mutiny on my boat I was cleared in court but deemed insane. **Captain Queeg**

ANAGRAMS

Have the tangled words on a blackboard or printed on cards. Give a clue. Allow one minute for players to write an answer. Then erase the word from the blackboard or put down the card. If done orally, have a scorekeeper to determine who makes the first and most correct answers. If written, answers may be checked.

A flower—rccosu—**crocus**
An insect—eeetlb—**beetle**
A city in the U. S. A.—anntncicii—**Cincinnati**
A musical instrument—liepsnekcolg—**glockenspiel**
A fruit—reiompsmn—**persimmon**
An occupation—emcnahci—**mechanic**
A color—aevum—**mauve**
A number—ittenerh—**thirteen**
A kind of tree—ltaaacp—**catalpa**
Girl's name—eismasl—**Melissa**

SILLY SENTENCES

Give each contestant a list of words each of which must be used in a sentence. Each contestant has a different list if desired but all may use the same. One giving the silliest sentence wins. Suppose the words, written on a blackboard or a card, are: cow, roof, necklace, burglar, banana, radio. The sentence might be: The necklace on the banana eating a cow turned on the radio scaring away the burglar who was stealing the roof.

FAMOUS ANIMALS

ORAL QUIZ

A cat who went to London with his master. **Dick Whittington's cat**

Its industry and perseverance taught a great patriot a lesson. **Spider—Robert Bruce**

Just by raising my foot once I started a blaze. **Mrs. O'Leary's cow**

By warning many people I became a hero in Colonial days. **Paul Revere's horse**

I nearly starved, not even a bone to eat, but I laughed later. **Mother Hubbard's dog**

I crossed the bridge and didn't care who lived under it. **Great Big Billy Goat Gruff**

Having done all the work others refused to do naturally I didn't share the results of my labors. **Little red hen**

I, smarter than my brothers, kept a kettle of boiling water on the fire, just for intruders. **The little pig**

Aeronautic steeds, who fly once a year, make children happy. **Santa's reindeer**

I may be small, but, oh boy, am I smart! I freed a lion and made a good friend. **The mouse that chewed the ropes from the lion**

True, I once gulped down a man, but I'm no criminal. I let him out. **The whale that swallowed Jonah**

A man once helped me when I had a sore foot. Years later I helped him, even though I was supposed to kill him. **The lion befriended by Androcles**

PROVERBS

Complete these proverbs and old sayings. Call on the person whose hand is raised first. An incorrect answer puts the player out of the game. The leader may, if desired, call upon the players in regular order.

It's a long lane—**that has no turning.**
Haste—**makes waste.**
Never put off till tomorrow—**what you can do today.**
It's never too—**late to mend.**
The longest way—**round is the shortest way home.**
Necessity is—**the mother of invention.**
He who hesitates—**is lost.**
A barking dog—**never bites.**
A penny saved—**is a penny earned.**
Don't count your—**chickens before they're hatched.**
A rolling stone—**gathers no moss.**
Fair weather cometh—**out of the north.**
Man is born unto trouble as—**the sparks fly upward.**
Don't cross a bridge—**until you come to it.**
Wealth maketh—**many friends.**
Wisdom is better than—**rubies.**
Where there is no vision—**the people perish.**
A barking dog is better—**than a dead lion.**
Familiarity breeds—**contempt.**
The gods help them that—**help themselves.**
Continual dropping wears away—**a stone.**
I fear the Greeks even when—**bearing gifts.**
Nothing is stronger—**than custom.**
It makes a difference whose—**ox is gored.** (Luther)
Speak the truth and—**shame the devil.** (Cervantes)

FAIRY TALES

From the clue given, name the fairy tale. Answers may be oral or written.

They crossed over the bridge. **Three Billy Goats Gruff**

A bean planter. **Jack and the Bean Stalk**

Two abandoned children meet a witch. **Hansel and Gretel**

An animal that never went barefooted. **Puss in Boots**

A little chap who wouldn't tell his name. **Rumpelstiltzken**

A girl who kept house for seven. **Snowwhite and the Seven Dwarfs**

The belle of the ball. **Cinderella**

Saved by the woodcutters. **Red Riding Hood**

He would have astonished the barber. **Bluebeard**

She grew better looking with age. **The Ugly Duckling.**

She sold something for smokers. **Little Match Girl**

You have to strike it to make it work. **The Tinder Box**

It paid them to keep a kettle on the fire. **Three Little Pigs**

These children were blanketed by birds. **Babes in the Woods**

A sovereign who loved gold. **Midas**

BE AN ORATOR

Have the players pick a piece of paper from a hat. On each paper is the name of a subject on which one who draws the paper must talk for five minutes. Use absurd and meaningless subjects. The player who talks the longest wins. Subjects: Who cares? If it isn't. It all depends. Summer is more than a mile . . . Who fried the popcorn? The real truth is . . . Cows in the icebox. How old is old? Not me. After all. Nobody you know. Never mind. Oh, no!

TELL ME A STORY

Players sit in a circle. The leader stands in the center and tells them they are about to compose a story to which each player must contribute at least one sentence. Leader says he will start. He designates some-one in the circle to give the next sentence, and this is continued around the circle moving to the right, until all have given a sentence. Of course it is up to the last player to end the story with at least a grain of plausibility. The more silly the story, however, the better. For example:

It was midnight. It was a hot day in November. A horrible thing happened. Three lions, an angle worm, and a rhinoceros sat in the baby carriage. They ate the baby in one mouthful. Suddenly an eagle swooped down and ate the animals. The baby's father saw the eagle and got his gun. The gun backfired and scared away a tribe of Indians. The eagle dropped the baby from the top of a cliff ten miles high. The baby landed safely on top of a sharp rock. He laughed because he was alone. He hated people around talking baby talk to him. The father heard the baby laughing. He brought him home in time for this twenty-first birth-day party.

ACCORDING TO HOYLE
OR
YOU CAN'T WIN

Deal cards from a bridge deck, one at a time, until all are distributed. Do not have more than thirteen players besides the leader, so that each player will have at least two cards. Leader asks those with the four aces and those with the four deuces to come up. Each ace names a stunt for the deuce of his suit to do. Then the kings and the treys come up, and follow the same procedure. Next queens and four spots, and so on down to the eights and fives. The crazier the stunts the better. Suggested ones: Name the presidents of the U. S. A. in order with no pauses and no errors; walk across the room on your hands; sing one verse of any song you choose, omitting every other word and keeping the tune; eat an apple faster than any other person selected by the group; jump up and hit both heels behind your back with your hands; see if you can jump higher than any other person selected by the group; _and so on.

WHIRLING DERVISHES

This stunt is not for people who become dizzy easily. Two players start at one end of the room and see who can reach the other end first, whirling about rapidly all the way.

MOTHER GOOSE TODAY

Answers may be oral or written. One with the most correct answers wins.

Who sang in a night club for his food? **Tommy Tucker**

Who was an acrobat? **Jack-be-Nimble**

Who stole meat and started in business? **Taffy, the Welshman**

Who brought a blow gun from Mars? **The Little Man with the Gun**

Who, being no snob, lays eggs for everybody? **Higgledy-Piggledy**

What pair, after a fall, became famous ski-jumpers? **Jack and Jill**

Who answers questions on the radio, but admits he's stupid? **Simple Simon**

Who invented a pocket that comes back if you lose it? **Lucy Locket**

Who is now a florist with a wonderful garden? **Mistress Mary**

Who is a big business man with his thumb in a lot of things? **Jack Horner**

DROP THE HANDKERCHIEF

The victim puts both hands on the floor. His knees are at his elbows. Someone drops a handkerchief in front of him and he must pick it up with his teeth.

BLACK AND BLUE

This needs two teams, two leaders and a judge. The judge says, "We hear and use the expression 'black and blue' very often. I wonder how many things we know that are actually black or blue. The leader of team one will name something black. The leader of team two will do the same, and so on down both lines. Then we shall start again naming things that are blue. Any member of a team making a mistake, naming something already said, or failing to answer at once will have to sit down. The team with the fewest mistakes wins. If both teams have a perfect score, we shall be surprised."

Teams will probably use such words as:

black night	black mark	blue blood
black cat	blue sky	blue book
black look	blue bird	blue Danube
black cloud	blue flower	etc.

The catch is in not naming the same thing twice as black bird and blue bird, black dress and blue dress, etc.

JUMP OVER THE PENCIL

Put a pencil on the floor. Have the contestant stand so that his toes almost touch the pencil. Then tell him to bend over, grasp the front of his toes, and jump over the pencil while still holding on to his toes.

GUESS WHO

Each player, in turn, tells others who she isn't, although she may resemble that person. Players try to guess who she is. Player may say, "I have a famous beard and I am wicked but I am not Bluebeard." Blackbeard. "I had a long sleep but I am not Rip Van Winkle." The Sleeping Beauty. "I was in the water a long time but I am not Moby Dick." The Ancient Mariner. "I am a princess who saved a commoner's life." Pocahontas. "I have the name of a bird but I did not sing, I cared for the sick." Florence Nightingale.

THAT AIN'T THE WAY I HEERD IT

Players sit in a circle, not too close together. They are told before beginning the game that a short message, just received on the telephone, will be whispered to them by the person on their right. They must repeat the message, changing just one word. When the message gets back to the beginner he says it aloud and remarks in astonishment, "That ain't the way I heerd it!" He then gives the original message. For example, the original message might be: "John Smith shot his wife with a cannon last night." The next person may whisper, "John Brown shot his wife with a cannon last night." Third, "Betty Brown shot his wife with a cannon last night." Fourth, "Betty Brown shot my wife with a cannon last night." Fifth, "Betty Brown shot my goldfish with a cannon last night." Sixth,

"Betty Brown shot my goldfish near a cannon last night." Seventh, "Betty Brown shot my goldfish near a cannon last year." Eighth, "Betty Brown scared my goldfish near a cannon last night." Ninth, "Betty Bullet scared my goldfish near a cannon last night." Tenth, "Betty Bullet scared my wife near a cannon last night." Eleventh, "Betty Bullet scared my wife near a camel last night." Twelfth, "Betty Bullet scared my wife with a camel last night." Thirteenth, "Betty Bullet socked my wife with a camel last night," and so on, growing sillier with each sentence.

IN MY GARDEN

The players guess the flower spoken about. The one guessing the most correctly and first wins. The gardener gives hints like this: In my garden are these flowers—
Part of your eye. **Iris**
It can be worn. **Lady slipper**
He preaches. **Jack-in-the-pulpit**
Remember me. **Forget-me-not**
This one is a vain animal. **Dandelion**
This one must have been shot. **Bleeding heart**
An early riser. **Rose**
This one goes with bonds. **Stocks**
He'll kill us. **Crocus—croak us**
A country noted for its autos. **Carnation**

TAKE A NUMBER

Have the answers telling why these dates or numbers are famous, seeing who can answer the most first and correctly.

1066—Battle of Hastings
1492—Columbus discovered America
??—Use birth date of some guest
4—Horsemen of the Apocalypse
3—Three Blind Mice
10—Ten little Indians
360—Degrees in a circle
21—Voting age
4 and 20—Blackbirds baked in a pie
40—Life begins at forty

RIDDLES. A CONTEST

Give a prize to the one who asks the best riddle, whether it can be answered or not. Following are some suggestions:

1. Why is it easier to be a clergyman than a doctor? **It's easier to preach than to practice.**

2. What things increase the more you contract them? **Debts.**

3. How do bees dispose of their honey? **They sell (cell) it.**

4. Why is a large coat like a banana skin? **Both are easy to slip on.**

5.   How long did Cain hate his brother?   **As long as he was able.   (Abel.)**

6.   What's the difference between a hill and a pill? **A hill is hard to get up and a pill is hard to get down.**

7.   What is full of holes and yet holds water?   **A sponge.**

8.   Why is dough like the sun?   **When it rises it is light.**

9.   What does a commercial artist like to draw best? **His salary.**

10.   What roof covers the most noisy tenant?   **The roof of the mouth.**

LOOK MA, NO ARMS

A boy lies flat on his back, his body stretched out straight, his arms folded on his chest.   He rises to a sitting position without unfolding the arms or using the elbows.   When he gets in a sitting position he bends one leg under his body.   Then, on this knee, he can easily reach a standing position.

NOT A CAMEL—JUST A THREAD

The player sits on a jug or a milk bottle and tries to thread a needle, not too small a one, with a black thread, while the others count to twenty.

STRANGE PETS

This is an oral game, just to see who can answer first and best. Leader gives a definition. Contestants raise their hands and are called on.

Part of a blossom—**PETal**
Found in a band—**TrumPET**
Comes from wells—**PETroleum**
Wants your name signed—**PETition**
A small pet—**PETty**
A sea rover—**PETral**
Will become stone—**PETrify**
Is bad tempered—**PETulant**
You get hoisted on this one—**PETard**
Women wear it—**PETticoat**

TONGUE TWISTERS

Have these sentences printed on slips of paper. Give a prize to the player who can read one without hesitation, repeating, laughing, or a mistake.

1. Theo thought Telamachus Thimblebum was copper bottoming the poultry pots but he was aluminiuming them thoroughly.

2. Sylvester Socklesteiner seldom separates syllabubs from syllables but Saturday seemed strangely significant for Sylvester slowly but slovenishly stopped separating and started slushing.

3. Glamorous Cordelia calmly concentrates curiously and curtly on contemplating catastrophes commemorating casual cornucopias culled from centipedes

and choreographers, who can't corroborate.

4. Pedagogues peruse ponderous encyclopedical pamphlets searching for stupendous scintillating segments of psychological phraseology, vicious vicinity, and loquacious, pugnacious, peevish people.

5. Nebuchadnezzar never knew Nnaam, Nicodemus nor notary neophytes, nevertheless neutrality nonchalantly nonparticipating normally nullified numismatic nystagmus.

6. Setaceous sesquipedalian sentences satiate Saturnian scarabs scarifying scintillating scoffers suddenly.

7. Thaddeus takes thamaturgy, telephotography, theogony, thermodynamics, tintinnabulation and troglodytic tropology at college and will gradually graduate when he's ninety.

BUS SERVICE

Each player takes the name of a large or important city in the United States. They compare notes to make certain no two have the same name. Then the Station Master is called in. Players form a circle and he is in the center. He announces which bus is leaving, where from, and its destination. If there are no two players with the names of those cities he must try again. If he calls cities that are represented those two change places and he attempts to get to one of the places first. The one left out becomes the Station Master. If the Station Master fails after five attempts, he is out of the game.

PUT THE COWS IN THE BARN

This game is played like the Ant Hill. The answers all begin with the letters C-o-w.

A scared cow. **COWard**
A poetic cow. **COWper**
One that is poisonous. **COWbane**
One that flies. **COWbird**
This one rides on a track. **COWcatcher**
One that tends other cows. **COWherd**
A tuft of hair much awry. **COWlick**
A monk's hood. **COWl**
Blooms in meadows. **COWslip**
Lives in Russia. **MosCOW**
Lives on the water. **S-COW**
A battle was once fought here. **COWpens**

FIRST NAMES

Identify these people by their first names. The leader gives the first name. The first person to guess the full name correctly scores a point. The winner is the one with the most points. Suggested first names and a clue are offered by the leader.

Walt—(Whitman) a writer
Daniel—(Boone) a great hunter
Henry—(Hudson) an explorer
John—(Smith) nearly scalped
Thomas—(Edison) turned on the lights
Betsy—(Ross) stitched a famous bit of cloth
Annie—(Laurie) I'd die for her
Mary—(Baker Eddy) founded a religion

Alexander—(Graham Bell) call me up some time
Sarah—(Bernhardt) she loved the theatre
Florence—(Nightingale) known for her good works
Joe—(McCarthy) point of order
Edna—(Ferber) wrote So Big
Dwight—(Eisenhower) good golfer
Robert—(Peary) get your fur coat
George—(Dewey) sailed the seas
Jack—(Benny) plays the violin and save money
George—(Gobel) you can't hardly find comedians
like him no more

SIAMESE HOPTOADS

Two couples do this stunt at the same time, each
couple standing back to back, hands joined. The
couples stand at opposite ends of the gym or room. At
a signal each couple hops across the room, or gym,
turns, and hops back to the original position. The
couple wins who gets back to the starting point first.

MOTHER GOOSE MEMORIES

Players take turns saying Mother Goose rhymes.
The one who fails to remember a rhyme is out. There
must be no repetition. This is best for a small group.

JUMPING JEHOSEPHAT

The actor tells the audience his name is Jumping Jehosephat and he can do wonderful things. He requests the audience to pile up anything they please, as high as they please. No matter how many objects or how high they are piled he can simply take off his hat and jump over it. After the pile is arranged he removes his hat, puts it on the floor, and jumps over it.

WHAT DAY IS IT?

Ask somebody to put a paper on his forehead, using a little paste to make it stick, and write the name of the day of the week on the paper, with a lead pencil or pen. It is not so easy as it sounds.

THE MYSTERY VOICE

Blindfold the contestant, and place others in a circle around him. People in a circle move around after the blindfolding so there is no chance of the contestant remembering who stands where. Someone in the circle sings a few bars of a song. The one blindfolded must guess who the singer was. If he guesses correctly, he and the singer change places. If he has ten failures in his guessing, the one blindfolded is out of the game.

THE FOUR STORY TELLERS

Four players stand side by side, facing the audience. Number one tells any lively story, like Little Jack Horner, or The Cat and the Fiddle. If a longer story is desired, it may be read. Number two does facial expressions appropriate to the story, as Number One has an absolutely dead pan face. Number three makes wild gestures that go with the story. Number four makes appropriate sounds, as if it is the story of Mother Hubbard, the barking of the dog, his laughter, and so on.

THE GREAT TUMBLER

Fill a glass tumbler nearly full of water. Place it across your hand, on your palm, at shoulder level. Have fingers point forward, thumb out, elbows close to side. Move the hand containing the glass under the arm pit, making as much of a circle as possible in doing so. Keep the glass on the palm of your hand. Return to starting position with no water spilled.

JUST A PICK-UP

The contestant stands on one foot, holds the other foot behind him with one hand and with his teeth picks up a sheet of paper that is placed on the floor in front of him.

WATER RACE

Place a large bowl filled with water on the table between the two contestants. Each has an empty glass before him. He is given a teaspoon and must fill the empty glass with water from the bowl, a spoonful at a time. The one who fills his glass first is given a nice cold drink.

CALLING CONTEST

Players are each given a card on which is the name of the animal whose call they must imitate. They do the calls singly at first. After a prize is awarded to the best caller, all repeat the calls together. The one who gets the name giraffe of course makes no noise but just stretches up his neck. It is fun to guess what animals are imitated before a prize is awarded.

HOW'S YOUR AIM?

On the floor in front of the player place an empty quart milk bottle. The player stands erect with his right arm extended straight out from his shoulder so it is directly over the bottle. With his left hand he picks up a metal hair curler or a clothespin and drops it into the bottle. The game is to see which player can drop the most objects into the bottle in a given time. Have a pile of curlers or clothespins on the table.

TOREADOR

Two boys, covered with a dark blanket and having a cardboard bull's head attached to the front of the first boy, and with a rope tail at back of the blanket, do a dance. They back up to the wall and the bull scratches his back. He bows to the audience. Someone holds a flower up and he smells of it. He does anything he thinks of, sits down, bellows, etc.

MAKE YOUR OWN WORDS

Print on a blackboard or a sheet of paper where all can see any ten letters. Give players ten minutes in which to make words from these letters, using each letter once only in a word. Take the letters Y-M-A-S-T-Z-P-U-L-G. Words might include nasty, plug, zary, zany, Uz, apt, etc.

CORNER TO CORNER

A player, blindfolded, is placed in each corner of the gym or room. Each one must cross to the corner diagonally across from him without running into or touching other contestants. The one who reaches his corner first without accident wins.

HE'S STUNTED

A mother comes out with a lad looking very limp, as does the mother. She tells the audience her boy is stunted and will never grow large and strong because he's been on so many silly stunt programs he's worn out. She names a number of stunts he has done. As she names them he does them. If any equipment is needed for the stunts, a girl brings it from behind a screen. The boy may jump, run, march, turn cart-wheels, etc. When he is through he drops to the floor exhausted. The girl and his mother take him by the arms and drag him off the stage.

WHAT A PAIR!

Have an even number of players. Give each a card. On half of the cards is written the first name of some celebrity. On the other half of the cards is the surname of one of these celebrities. When the cards are assembled properly you have the full names of the celebrities. Each guest must find his or her partner by finding the name that goes to complete what is on his or her card. Suggested names: Charlotte Corday, Davy Crockett, Lionel Barrymore, Frank Buck, Clark Gable, Lillie Langtry, Christopher Columbus, Perle Mesta, John Smith, Jeanne D'Arc.

ALL TOGETHER—GO

One player is IT. He goes out of the room while the others decide on some well-known proverb or saying. Each player is given one word of this proverb. Of course this means several players may have the same word. Suppose the proverb chosen is "It's a long lane that has no turning." The one who is IT is called in. The others form a circle around him. When he says **READY** each player shouts his word loudly. It will take great skill on the part of the one who is **IT** to sort out the words and guess what the proverb is. Take turns until each one has been the guesser.

COLORS

Use each of these colors with a word usually associated with it. Write answers as rapidly as possible. Leader says each word but once. The first one through wins if answers are plausible. Contestants may write down a word and come back to it later for the associated word if there is time. This may be done orally.

brown—study	lilac—time
purple—hills	blue—sky
emerald—isle	red—light
green—thumb	silver—threads
yellow—moon	rosy—prospects

FRONT AND BACK

Players sit in a circle and are told by the leader that they have just one chance. The beginner will name any word of two syllables. The next player must use the second syllable of the word mentioned, add a syllable to it and make another word. It is sound rather than spelling that counts. Player who takes more than a half-minute to make a correct word is out.

Examples: Oyster—stirring; ringlet—letter; ermine—mingle; gullet—lettuce; tussling—ingot; etc.

OUT OF REACH

Dare a member of the group to put his right hand where his left hand can't reach it. If he fails, show him how. Put your right hand on your left elbow.

UPS AND DOWNS

All players, who are numbered, stand in a line or circle while the leader, in front of the line or in the center of the circle, counts loudly, after explaining to the players that when an odd number is named all players with odd numbers must stoop down, rising quickly. Those with even numbers stoop down at even numbers. At zero or any number ending in zero all stand still. Leader counts rapidly and the number are not named in order.

WHAT DOES IT MEAN?

Ask a player to name four words beginning, respectively, with a, b, c, and d, that other players may not be able to define. If players can define the given words the beginner must take four other letters and try it again. If they cannot define the words he chooses someone to take his place. Words like these might be used: 1. atheneum—library, 2. balbriggan—knitted cotton fabric, 3. cuneiform—wedgeshaped, 4. defenestration—murder by hurling people out of windows.

SHAKE HANDS, PARTNER

Players stand in a circle. Two are blindfolded, turned around several times, taken out of the circle and placed in the center and told to meet and shake hands.

ADD A LETTER

The leader tells the players that the letter added to the word to make another word must be a vowel. May be prefixed, added at end or inserted. Give players a paper with words printed on it. Have a time limit and see who gets through first with correct words. For example:

sing—singe	lot—loot	rid—raid
cut—cute	gilt—guilt	shut—shout
pal—pail	got—goat	bat—bait

OVER AND ABOVE

The leader faces the players who have been told to imitate the rapid movements of his hands and arms up in the air. When the leader can think of nothing new to do he calls on another to take his place. The leader may wave his arms over his head, clasp his hands over his head, move his arms as if a windmill, clap his hands over his head, grasp the elbows over his head, put a hand on the top of his head, put his hands on his shoulders, stretch his arms and hands out straight, wring the hands in front of his face, etc.

NAME HER HUSBAND

Name, without hesitation, the instant called on, the following husbands mentioned in the Bible.

Eve—Adam   Abigail—Nabal
Rachel—Jacob   Hannah—Elkanah
Bathsheba—Uriah   Rebekah—Isaac
Hagar—Abraham   Sarah—Abraham
Eunice—Paul   Jezebel—Ahab
Vashti—Ahasuerus   Athalia—Jehorum
Delilah—Samson   Hepzibah—Hezekiah
Bernice—Agrippa

WHAT DOES THIS MEAN?

A couple is sent out of the room to prepare a list of words which they will ask the players to define. In the meantime the players decide on a definition of a word given them by the leader. This definition must be used in answer to any question asked. For example, the question might be, "What is an echo?" The answer might be, "The shortest way home," if the word given by the leader was "long." If the couple sent out can guess the word given by the leader they score one. Another couple is sent out. Use unusual words, such as bubble, sneeze, anemia, cardiograph, etc.

SCRAMBLED VERSE

On slips of paper have written the words of one line of a well-known poem, scrambled. Give out one slip at a time and give the player but two minutes in which to re-assemble the words. Make as many cards or slips as there are players, each slip different or, if desired, make a copy of each card for each player. No capitals.

to wait learn to and labor/Learn to labor and to wait.
                                        —Longfellow
is last painted when picture Earth's/When Earth's last picture is painted.   —Kipling
out chilling clouds the the that of wind came/That the wind came out of the cloud, chilling.   —Poe

BE A POET

Two teams vie with each other in composing poetry. The leader gives any line, such as "It was a windy, snowy day." The team that first gives a rhyming next line wins one point. The leader gives out lines until one team gains at least ten points. All lines must be strictly original and the sillier the better.

LAST BUT NOT LEAST

The leader names any four-legged animal. The one on whom he calls then names an animal whose name begins with the last letter of the one named by the leader, and so on. Those who fail to name an animal promptly must pay a forfeit. For example: aardvark, kangaroo; otter, rabbit; tiger, rat; etc.

FAMOUS NAMES

The stunt is to name two famous people with the same first name. The leader points a finger at someone who must answer immediately. For example: Daniel Boone and Daniel Webster; John Alden and John Paul Jones.

DO YOUR STUNT

Call on each player to do a different stunt. Give a prize to one who, in the opinion of the majority of guests, does his stunt best. For example, these stunts may be assigned:
1. Sing the alphabet, selecting your own tune.
2. Give a greeting in at least three languages.
3. Count from 1 to 100 as if making a very tragic speech.
4. Walk around the room as if you were a ghost.
5. Take ten skips backward.
6. Imitate any radio actor or actress named by the leader.
7. Imitate the sound of as many farm animals as possible.
8. Make a silhouette of any designated person using scissors and cardboard in three minutes.

NAME THE IMPS

Twelve people, wearing pointed paper caps on heads, represent the Imps. They pantomime their names which the players must guess, writing the names on cards. The winner is the one guessing the most names correctly. For example: Impair, Impale, Impart, Impatient, Impede, Impel, Imperative, Implement, Implore, Impolite, Important, Improve. All these words are easily pantomimed.

WHAT'S MY PROFESSION?

Have the guests dressed to portray their selected profession. Give each one a number. Then pass out paper and pencil to each, telling the players to write the number of each guest and what profession they represent. Use as unusual professions as possible. For example:—

a—Detective—has a spyglass, takes notes, looks sharply at everybody and everything.

b—School teacher—wears spectacles and a worried look, carries books and papers.

c—Traffic cop—blows a whistle and directs the traffic, waving his arms wildly.

d—A doctor—wears a white cap, a gown, and a stethoscope.

e—Fortune teller—carries a crystal ball.

f—Actress—makes wild gestures and poses dramatically.

g—Lawyer—man with a brief case.

h—Humorist—man with a very sad expression. He is accompanied by another man who laughs all the time.

i—Paper boy—carries an imaginary bundle of papers under his arm and appears to be calling loudly.

IT'S A LAUGH

Have a contest to see who can tell the funniest story. Then have the winner tell a sad story.

THREE AT A TIME

The contestant must do three different things at once, anything he wishes to attempt. He may whistle, dance, sweep the floor, laugh, jump, wave his hands, cry, crawl, scratch. The contestant who does the funniest or most difficult three things wins a prize.

ONCE UPON A TIME

The player is given ten minutes in which to tell a story beginning with the words, "Once upon a time," and ending with "And they lived happily ever after." A subject is assigned him—as silly a one as possible. For example: an angle worm; lipstick; litter bug; aspirin tablet.

PIED PROVERBS

The contestant must complete a proverb, begun by the leader, with the ending of another proverb. The one giving the funniest answers and the quickest ones wins a prize.

It's a long lane—but few are chosen.

He who fights and runs away—is the shortest way home.

It's an ill wind—that has no turning.

Better late—for tomorrow we die.

Don't count your chickens till—the well runs dry.

IMITATION IS FLATTERY

Imitate the following everyday happenings in pantomime: A turtle on its back; a rooster crowing at dawn;
a willow in the wind; a caterpillar becoming a butterfly;
a Boy Scout after his first long hike, etc. Subjects may
be selected by the contestants. The audience guesses
what happening is portrayed.

MIND READER

Tell the audience you and your assistant can give
them the name of any person present that they may
select. You leave the room and the audience selects a
person. Your assistant is pledged not to mention the
name to you but he will convey the knowledge in a
mysterious fashion; you will read his mind. Choose
your assistant, take him aside and tell him you will ask
him three questions. The first two words in his answers
must begin with the initials of the person selected. If
the person chosen is named Mary Norton, the question
could be, "How old is your niece?" The answer might
be, "Merely nine but she acts twenty." The next question might be, "Where will you spend your vacation?"
He may answer, "Maine—nothing like the climate up
there." Lastly you might ask, "When do you sleep
best?" He would reply, "Midnight—noon—any old
time." You will see all answers have first two words
beginning with M. N. Look over the group and see
who has those initials.

A SAD STORY OF YOUNG LOVE

Someone reads the story while the noises are made offstage or from behind a screen.

Marietta walked (1) in the park as the darkness dropped (2) down. She listened to the soft music (3) of the night. A wave of remembrance swept (4) over her. The soft murmur (5) of the night birds made her heart sing. (6) Gently the wind whispered (7) in the willows? Her spirits fell. (8) She felt sad. Somewhere in her memory a bell rang (9) softly. She thought of her romantic lover, Leslie, who used to greet her every evening with sweet words. (10) She remembered how he used to roll his eyeballs (11) in delight as he looked at her. Then, as she realized she would never see him again, her heart was torn (12) with pain. Suddenly she heard his gentle voice as of old. (13) He softly approached. (14) He kissed her gently. (15) Then they slowly walked (16) home through the park, hand in hand, two loving hearts beating as one. (17) And the wind whispered (18) in the willows. The birds sang softly, (19) and the night was filled with sweet music. (20)

Sounds: 1. heavy tramping; 2. heavy weight drops; 3. loud jazz tune is played; 4. swishing sound made by brooms; 5. loud cackling and crowing, hoot of owls; 6. beat of drums; 7. sound of electric fans; 8. weight drops as before; 9. loud clang of bell; 10. loud rough voice yells, "Hey, kid"; 11. heavy balls rolled over the floor; 12. sound of ripping cloth; 13. rough voice again yells, "Hey, kid"; 14. heavy stumbling steps; 15. loud smacking sound; 16. sound of running feet; 17. two drums beating loudly in unison; 18. sound of electric fans as before; 19. repeat sounds of five; 20. loud jazz as before, ending with all previous sounds repeated in unison.

IDENTIFY THE PRISONER

A jury, seated at a table, is blindfolded. The Judge brings in the prisoner who is to be identified. Each jury member may ask two questions. The prisoner may answer or the Judge may answer for him. The prisoner may clap his hands or play the mouth organ instead of speaking. The jurors at any time may guess as to prisoner's identity. If, after all have asked questions and guessed, the prisoner is still unidentified the jurors remove their blindfolds and see who it is.

NAME THE TUNE

A player with a good voice hums old tunes, or new and other players must name the tune. The player naming the most tunes correctly wins the prize.

FAMOUS LIVING PEOPLE

Actors may speak or pantomime action common to one impersonated. For example, one posing as Liberace would smile, pantomime piano playing. One posing as John Gambling would represent the name by pantomiming dealing cards or throwing dice. Garbo would don dark glasses, pull hair over her cheeks and mutter, "I want to be alone." Hedda Hopper could wear a crazy hat.

TAKE A WALK?

A couple stand in the center of the room, close together, facing in opposite directions. They join arms and try to walk to the end of the room, each struggling to move the other player in his direction. As a consequence they jerk back and forth vainly but at last give it up unless one player is much stronger than the other.

EASY DOES IT

The leader tells one of the players he is *Easy* and must do as he is told. The leader names the stunts, such as running around in a circle backward three times, stopping where you began. Then the other players may ask *Easy* to do stunts. When *Easy* has carried out four orders successfully he may appoint another player to be *Easy*.

A WOMAN IN THE HOUSE

The leader announces that there is a famous woman in the house and they must guess who she is. Each player may ask three questions of the leader or, if desired, a player may act as the famous woman by just standing up and answering questions. Each player may ask three questions and have one guess. The one who guesses the identity of the woman may become the leader. Suggested names are: Pocahontas, Queen Elizabeth, Mother Hubbard, Cleopatra, etc.

TELL ME

Seat the players in couples. The leader has prepared a list of very personal questions. The person who is asked the question does not answer but the partner does. Have a man and woman as partners. The one who answers does so as if the question referred to him or to her. A man is asked, "What is your most expensive habit?" The woman replies, "Having a new permanent every six weeks." She is asked, "What is your favorite sport?" and he answers, "Boxing."

I MADE MY WILL

Each player is given a slip of paper on which is written a bequest and another slip of paper on which is written the reason for such bequest. These slips are well shuffled before being passed out. Each player decided upon a member of the group to be the recipient of his bequest. When called upon he stands and reads from his slips, filling in the name of the receiver. For example: "I will to Miss —— my poor old classmate, my bald head, because I never use it."

QUAINT QUARTET

This needs four singers who render a familiar song, each one singing the song in a different key and a different tempo.

Section Three

Action and Musical Stunts

SOLOMON'S SEALS
(*An animal act*)

Any even number of boys are dressed in brown seal suits, which may be made of gunny sacks, denim, old flannel shirts, etc., with flippers attached. Whiskers are painted on upper lips or are made of straw and glued on.

The trainer is a tall, dignified older boy, who wears a high silk hat, white trousers and shoes, and a red coat.

The TRAINER *enters before the curtain and addresses the audience.*

TRAINER. Ladies and gentlemen, you are about to see Solomon's Seals—the most intelligent, the most amazing, the most versatile seals in all the world. They understand perfectly every word their trainer, Mr. Septimus Solomon, says to them, and they obey directions with military precision, as you shall see. I am Mr. Septimus Solomon.

TRAINER *goes off at left, and the curtain rises to show the seals lying on their stomachs in a circle on stage.* TRAINER *enters from left, stands at left, and starts the performance.*

TRAINER. Seals, attention. (*The seals raise their heads and look at him.*) At ease. (*The seals flop back on their stomachs.)* Attention. *(Again the seals raise their heads and look at the* TRAINER.*)* How old are you? *(The seals clap their flappers three times each.)* Three years old; correct. Now go to sleep. *(The seals flop on their stomachs, heads down on the floor.)*

Attention. Sit up. *(The seals sit up very straight.)* Billy, will you balance a ball for us? *(The seal named Billy nods assent.* TRAINER *puts the ball on his nose, making it stick by means of glue on its side, and Billy apparently balances it as he waves his head, flippers, and body about.)* Very good, Billy. *(*TRAINER *takes the ball and replaces it in his pocket, while all the seals, even Billy, applaud heartily.)* Seals, do you like opera music? *(Seals shake their heads in violent dissent.)* Do you like dance music? Do you like *(name any popular cornet player)* ———? *(The seals nod assent and applaud violently.)* Sammy, you play a cornet solo for us, please. *(*TRAINER *gets a toy cornet from the wings and hands it to Sammy who plays "Cornet Chop Suey" or any other popular selection, music of course coming from a record offstage. When Sammy is through playing he hands the cornet to the* TRAINER *and the other seals applaud.)*

Good, Sammy. Now, everybody up in line. *(The seals form a straight line across the front of the stage, facing audience.)* Get acrobatic. *(The seals turn somersaults, stand on head, etc.)* Rest. *(The seals flop on their stomachs, as before.)* Now get in line and dance for us. *(The seals form a straight line as before and sway heads and flippers in time to the "Dance of the Comedians" or any other dance selection, coming from offstage.)* Rest. *(The seals flop on their stomachs, as before.)*

TRAINER. Attention. In line. *(The seals rise and stand in straight line, as before.)* Eyes right. *(The seals turn heads to right.*) Eyes left. (*The seals turn heads to the left.*) Eyes front. (*The seals gaze straight ahead.*) Is everybody happy? (*The seals shake their heads in dissent.* TRAINER *is surprised.*) You're not happy? Why not? (*The seals look at him reproachfully and rub their stomachs.*) Oh, you're hungry. Is that it? (*The seals nod assent.*) O.K. Speak. (*The seals give the weird bark or grunt common to seals.*)

Now you shall each have a nice big goldfish. (TRAINER *beckons off right, and a helper brings in a huge glass bowl filled with goldfish made from carrots, boiled just long enough to be soft, so they can be easily swallowed.*)

TRAINER. Eyes right. Attention. (*The seals turn sidewise to right in straight line, so the audience can see them really swallow the "fish."* TRAINER *takes the carrots, one by one, from the bowl and drops them into the open mouths of the seals. With practice the seals can catch the carrots if they are thrown toward their mouths. If some miss, others take the carrot from the floor and eat it.*) Are you happy now? (*The seals nod assent and applaud violently.*) Fine. Now say, "good-bye" to all the nice people. (*The seals face front, bow, wave their flippers, and bark.*)

CURTAIN

THE CIRCUS
(*An athletic stunt*)

The stage is set with a dark curtain as a backdrop. A big sign, "Tingling Brothers' Circus," is placed down extreme right, and a similar sign is fastened to the center of the backdrop.

The calliope enters at left and crosses to center, preceded by the leader, who wears a gay red suit and shako and carries a large baton. The calliope has eight boys for pipes. All wear long, straight, up-and-down gray gowns with gray caps on heads. Or bright yellow suits may be worn to indicate gilded pipes. The boys range themselves like organ pipes at center, and the leader stands in front of them and taps each boy on the head with his baton when it is his turn to sing a note. Thus, with each singing a separate note, they give the chorus of "Hail, Hail, the Gang's All Here," assisted by extras offstage, who hum the tune loudly. At the close of the song, the leader waves his baton, and the calliope moves to a position down right.

The Barker enters at left, bows to the audience, and takes his position down extreme left, from which post he announces the attractions as they appear. The players enter at right and go off at left.

BARKER. Parade of the clowns.

To music of "On Parade," the clowns enter at right, heavily made up and in as ridiculous suits as can be found. They go off at left.

BARKER. Hercula, the strong woman.

To the music of "National Emblem March," the strong woman, who is a small woman in sweater and skirt, enters and stands at center, while six men follow her, bring her properties, with much puffing and panting. When they have gone, she picks up the giant dumbell, which is a broomstick with a black ball stuffed with rags fastened to each end. She raises it above her head with an effort, then lowers it carefully. The 500-pound weight and the 1000-pound weight are made of cardboard and are marked in large black figures with their respective weights. She lifts them to shoulder height and sets them down. The iron bar is made of licorice. She picks it up, looks the audience in the eye, and playfully bites the air, showing her intention of biting the bar in two. With a great effort, she raises it to her lips and bites it in two. She bows to the applause, gathers up all her properties, stuffs them under one arm, and walks offstage.

BARKER. The two-headed girl.

Two girls march on the stage, each encircling the other's waist with one arm, while the other arm is thrust into the sleeve of a long, loose, gaily colored gown, which covers their feet. The gown is fastened about their waists with a wide sash, and a wide collar around their necks fastens in the back. They stop at the center of the stage, smile at the audience, and sing any sentimental song, gesticulating with their free arms. If they can do a little dance without falling over their feet, it will be very effective. At the close, they bow and shuffle off the stage.

BARKER. The tight rope walkers.

Two girls in short ruffled skirts and plain blouses in gay colors, with parasols to match, enter and walk an imaginary tight rope across the stage and back, to the music of "High Ridin'." They go off at left.

BARKER. The fat lady and her thin husband.

A large man, stuffed with pillows and dressed as a woman in a gown with a long skirt, a curled wig, and a fancy turban, enters with her husband. He is a tall, thin man on stilts, with long white trousers that cover the stilts, and a white sweater and cap. To the music of "Semper Fidelis March," they parade across the stage and go off at left.

BARKER. Our acrobats.

Any number of teen-age boys and girls in bright colored tights turn somersaults and cartwheels across the stage to the music of "Semper Fidelis March." After taking a bow, they run off at left.

BARKER. Our animals.

Any number of young people and adults, wearing Halloween animal suits, parade across the stage from left to right, to the music of "The Stars and Stripes Forever." They leave at left.

BARKER. And now the famous Tingling Brothers' Band.

Any number of band members, dressed in long red and green smocks and caps, enter, carrying toy instruments. They pretend to play "On Parade," but the music is really supplied by an off-stage record.

The calliope, which has remained down right, plays again, while all the actors reënter and parade across the stage, beginning with the clowns and ending with the band. The music is "Hail, Hail, the Gang's All Here," which may be either sung or played offstage by a record. At the close, the curtain falls.

BAG AND BAGGAGE
(*A military drill for girl guides and other hikers*)

This stunt requires any even number of girls in short skirts, white blouses, socks, sneakers, and very elaborate hair-dos, and a leader, who is a determined-looking young woman wearing a helmet and a brown suit and shoes. The girls all have knapsacks of brown material (stuffed shopping bags will do) over their shoulders. Each girl is wearing a large paper bag for a hat. All bags must be the same size and color and large enough to fit on the head but not too tightly.

The girls march on the stage behind their leader to the music of "Under the Double Eagle March." The leader stands at center as the girls form a circle around her, facing outward, and stand at attention. The leader gives directions rapidly, and the girls follow directions quickly.

LEADER.

Remove hats.

Change hats right.

(*Each girl puts her hat on the head of the girl at her right.*)

Tilt hats left.

Tilt hats right.

March three steps to right.

Change hats left.

Change hats right.

March three steps to left.

Change hats left.

Change hats right.

Mark time. 1, 2, 1, 2, 1, 2, 1, 2. Halt.
Face right. Form two lines.

(*The girls in the circle are all facing outward. When
told to form two lines those girls at the front half of
the circle, who are facing the audience, simply straighten
out to form a straight line instead of a curved one.
Those girls who are facing back of the stage turn right,
then face the front and straighten their line.*)

Stand back of your partner.

(*The girls in the back line move so they are directly
back of their respective partners in front.*)

Remove hats.
Change hats with partner.

(*Girls in front must not turn.*)

Change hats left.
Change hats right.
Change hats with partner.
Turn right, first row.
Turn left, second row.
March to form a line facing the front.

(*Second-row girls follow the first row, and they march
around the stage in a circle once, ending in straight
line across the front of the stage.*)

Stand at attention.
By now, the bags are wrecked, and so are the hair-dos.
Heads look as if they have never known a comb. The
leader looks at the girls in disgust.

LEADER. Left face. Back to camp and solitary confinement for gross untidiness. March!

The girls march offstage to the music of "Under the Double Eagle March," followed by the leader.

GLOWWORMS

(A specialty for revue)

The glowworms are any number of teen-age girls and an equal number of teen-age boys. The girls wear suits made of black net, with short ruffled skirts, long-sleeved blouses, round black caps, and black slippers and stockings. Around each girl's waist is a black sash, at the front of which is fastened securely a small electric battery or flashlight to give the glow which shines from a real glowworm's abdomen. The boys wear black net suits, with black gauze wings fastened to their shoulders, also long, tight black trousers and blouses, black sashes, and black slippers and stockings. If preferred, all suits may be a spectral blue or green. Black, however, is more effective.

The backdrop should show a moonlight scene, or a black cyclorama may be used. In the latter case, the stage should be dimly lighted with a few blue bulbs in the footlights.

To the music of "Glowworm," by Glinka, the girls and boys enter in couples at right, form a double circle at center, and march around in it clockwise.

All walk forward eight counts. Partners face and back four steps away from each other. Partners take four steps forward, toward each other. They link right arms, swing around four counts. Link left arms, swing around four counts. They walk forward eight counts. On the eighth count, each boy moves forward beside the girl in front of him. Repeat as often as desired. Then dancers march off left in straight line.

CY, THE PSYCHIATRIST

(*A mind-reading stunt*)

The stage is set as an office, with an entrance down
left.

A huge machine, constructed of boxes, black sheets,
screens, knobs, pipes, and bars, is at the center of the
stage.   A screen, presumably concealing a door, is at
the right end of the machine and a similar screen is at
the left end of the machine.   Behind the machine
and the two screens, the various groups of characters
change costumes.

The light and sound effects, as well as the music,
come from back of the machine. Use records for music.
For the music used, see the end of the book. Rapid
changes in costume will be needed, unless the people
who re-appear made over are represented by another
group of approximately the same size and appearance,
which is very difficult to accomplish. Have plenty of
room back of the machine and arrange costumes so that
garments may be added or removed, rather than have
extensive changes. Of course the more absurd the costumes are, the more effective they will be.

Cy is a tall, dignified man, who wears a dark business
suit and huge, tortoise-shell spectacles.   His voice is
slow, deliberate, and somewhat sinister.

When the curtain rises, Cy is standing by the machine.

Cy (*to the audience*).   In this machine you see the
greatest invention known to man—a machine that makes
you over into what you really want to be, down in the
bottom of your heart. I am Cyrus Sycamore, a professional mind healer, commonly known as Cy the Psy-

chiatrist. I look in your eyes, see what your ambition
is, and give it to you. My office hours are about to
begin.

The first group enter down left. The group consists of any number of dignified businessmen. Cy lines
them up, steps in front of them and stares long and
hard into their eyes. Then he waves them to the door
at the right of the machine. They troop meekly through
the door.

CY (*to the audience*). These men have longed for
years to emulate the Lone Ranger, ——— (*mentions a
famous movie portrayer of western rôles*), and other
heroes of the wide open spaces. They shall have that
pleasure for a short time. They'll be very happy—till
they get my bill next week.

Cy presses a knob on the machine. Lights go off and
come on, and there is a rumbling sound as of wheels
turning. It is produced by pulling a toy wagon back
and forth in the wings. The music of "The Last Round-
up" is played offstage. Cy presses another knob and
shuts off the machine. Lights cease to flicker, and the
music stops. The men who enter at right now emerge
at left, looking young and gay in cowboy attire, guns
and all. The music begins again, and the men sing "The
Last Round-up." Then they go off down left.

A group of spinsterish females, primly attired, enter
down left. Cy lines them up and looks them in the eye.
Then he motions them into the machine. They look
scared, but enter the door at right.

CY (*to the audience*). Ah! Those charming ladies
have always longed to be tap dancers—in a dignified
way, of course. Well, why not? But will they be stiff
tomorrow!

Cy turns on the machine as before. The music of Dvorak's "Humoresque" is heard. There is the same procedure as before. When Cy turns the machine off out come good-looking young women in short, frilly dresses. They do a tap dance, after which they exeunt down left. The music of "Swanee River" may be used for the dance.

A group of decrepit but well-dressed old men, with gray hair, enter down left. Each has a cane. The process of being stared at by Cy is very wearing on them, for they cannot stand up very well. They enter the machine at the wave of his hand, and he turns the knob.

Cy. Bless their dear old hearts! They always wanted to be acrobats, but they had to make money and become millionaires. They certainly have some fun coming to them. Here's where they get it!

The music of "Semper Fidelis March" begins as Cy turns on the machine. When he turns it off, out come handsome young men in tights and slippers, or slacks and loose blouses. They turn somersaults, play leap-frog, do a wheelbarrow race, and skin the snake. The wheelbarrow race is done by teams of two. One man is the wheelbarrow and moves himself by walking on his hands while his partner holds up his legs, grasping them by the ankles. Skin the snake is as follows: The first man stoops over and puts his right hand between his legs. Each man behind him stoops over and places his right hand between his legs and grasps the right hand of the man in front with his left hand. When all are in place, the last man in line lies on his back, and the line backs over him, the next man then lying down, and so on until every man is lying on his back. The last man to lie down then stands up and steps forward, each man in turn doing the same until all are in original position. This should be done very rapidly. Then the men hop off down left like jack rabbits.

The fourth group, made up of unattractive, bedraggled looking girls, enters down left. Cy seems puzzled as he looks into their eyes. He takes a long second look, then motions them into the machine and turns the knob.

Cy. Those weary-looking young ladies wish to be dramatic actresses. Well, why not? What have they got to lose?

The music of "Coronation March" from "Le Prophète" by Meyerbeer is heard. When the girls come out of the machine, they look stunning, with heavy make-up and long trailing black gowns. They line up and recite in concert, terribly and with extravagant gestures, Lady Macbeth's sleep-walking scene. As an encore, they do Wordsworth's poem, "Lucy Gray," making it as dramatic as Lady Macbeth. They go off down left.

The fifth group, composed of three men and three women, well dressed but slightly frivolous in appearance, enter down left. Cy gets a shock when he looks into their eyes. Finally he sends them into the machine.

Cy. And those charming but fuzzy-minded people— believe it or not—wish to be opera singers. What has opera ever done to people that people should do this to opera? However—! (*Shrugs.*)

To the music of the "Sextette" from "Lucia" by Donizetti, this group emerges from the machine, the men in black beards and long robes of black or purple, the women in Spanish, gypsy, and Japanese costumes, respectively. They sing the "Sextette," horribly of course. Then they sweep off down left in truly operatic fashion.

Cy (*shaking his head in sorrow*). When those poor,
deluded people wake up in the morning, they won't remember a single thing that happened. I hope you won't,
either. (*Bows to the audience and exits down left.*)

SIR CYRIL SEMAPHORE'S SINGERS
(*A song specialty*)

Sir Cyril is a tall, angular man, well dressed. As he
directs his singers, he moves his arms exactly like a
semaphore and his face is expressionless. The singers
are any number of young men, dressed in any desired
way, but all wearing small red or green berets. They
march in before the leader, as stiff-legged and mechan-
ically as puppets, swinging arms at their sides in perfect
unison. They line up and sing any songs they wish,
but varied in type, such as "Darling Nelly Gray,"
"Anvil Chorus," "Mandalay," and the latest juke-box
favorite. As they sing, they stand as stiff as boards,
eyes straight ahead, never looking at their leader, and
their arms move automatically in mechanical, meaningless gestures, exactly alike and in perfect unison. When
the songs are over, Sir Cyril bows, and the singers bow.
They turn and march off as stiffly as they entered, Sir
Cyril leading the way.

OFF TO THE RACES
(*An athletic stunt*)

The curtain rises to the music of "De Camptown Races," and reveals an empty stage. The music may continue softly throughout all the races. The BARKER, *a tall boy in white trousers, red jacket, and cap, enters at left and addresses the audience.*

BARKER. Today, honored guests, and—I hope—paying customers, you are about to participate in the opening of our wonderful new race track. Not the common race track for runners, bicycles, cars, horses. Oh, no! We are going to hold unique and fascinating races. There is no competition, as the term is generally understood. Instead, each racer attempts to beat his own record. However, the racer who receives the most applause at the close of the races wins a prize. The decision will be entirely up to you.

At left front of the stage is an easel facing the audience, and on the floor near the easel are eight signs. The Barker puts first sign on the easel. It reads: "EVENT 1—THE KANKAROO RACE."

Two boys enter at left, wearing one-piece gray sleeping suits covering hands and feet. On their heads are round caps with wired kangaroo ears. They stand, one behind the other, facing in the same direction. The one behind, Number 2, jumps on Number 1's back and locks his legs around Number 1's thighs. Number 1 now bends forward and rests his hands on the floor. Number 2, sitting on Number 1's back, leans over head on Number 1 and puts his hands on the floor. The same hand of each partner moves at the same time, and they walk across the stage on hands and feet. Number 2

must keep his legs securely fastened around Number
1, who keeps his knees as stiff as possible. Number 2
should be small and not too heavy to carry.

The Barker changes the sign to "EVENT 2—THE
DUCK RACE."

The ducks are any number of boys in yellow suits
and caps having orange brims. The feet and hand ex-
tensions on the suits are orange. Each duck squats as
low as possible and grasps his own heels outside his legs
from the back. The ducks run across the stage from
left to right, then offstage.

The Barker changes the sign to "EVENT 3—WAL-
RUS RACE."

The racing walruses wear dark brown suits and brown
caps, to which are attached cardboard tusks. Whiskers
may be pasted or painted on the face. The hand and
foot coverings are very large. Each walrus places his
hand on the floor back of the imaginary starting line
and stretches his legs straight out backward, extending
his body in a straight line from shoulders to heels.
Knees are held stiff, and the weight rests on hands and
toes. The walruses speed across the stage from left to
right and leave the stage.

The Barker changes the sign to "EVENT 4—FROG
RACE."

Any number of frogs wear green suits with yellowish
white fronts, and green caps on which are huge goggles.
Hand and foot coverings are sewed to represent web-
bing. Each frog squats and places his hands flat on
the floor about two feet in front of his webbed feet. His
knees do not touch the floor. From this position, he

springs forward a short distance, landing on his hands.
He quickly advances his feet close to but outside of his
hands. He lands in a squatting position, hands on the
floor. The frogs cross the stage from left to right, one
after the other, then go off.

The Barker changes the sign to "EVENT 5—ELE-
PHANT RACE."
Two elephants are represented by large boys who
wear gray suits and gray caps, to which are fastened
huge ears. Cardboard tusks are at the sides of the
cap, and a stuffed trunk dangles from the neck of each
elephant. The tails are short and fastened to the backs
of the suits. Each elephant bends forward, holding his
knees straight, and places his hands on the floor, keeping arms and legs perfectly stiff. Heads sway as the
elephants step. They travel slowly and cumberously
across the stage from left to right, then offstage.

The Barker changes the sign to "EVENT 6—THE
CRAB RACE."
The crabs are any number of boys in gray suits.
They wear gray caps, to which are attached by wires
round glass eyes. The crabs lie flat on their backs on
the floor at first. Then they raise themselves, pushing
their stomachs up and keeping arms and legs stiff.
They scramble across the stage sidewise, moving as
rapidly as possible, backs toward the floor, stomachs in
the air, and body supported by arms and legs, then
return to go offstage.

The Barker changes the sign to "EVENT 7—THE
LOBSTER RACE."
The lobsters are four boys in bright red suits and
caps. They place their backs over the imaginary start-

ing line, bend their knees, put hands on the floor behind them, elbows straight, heads are pointed toward the left of the stage and feet toward the right. They travel backward, from left to right, only hands and feet touching the floor.

The Barker changes the sign to "EVENT 8—THE RABBIT RACE."

Any number of rabbits may be used. They may be boys or girls in brown suits and long-eared caps, with tiny cotton tails fastened to their backs. They get down on all fours and hop rapidly across the stage, then go off.

BARKER. And now, my friends, you shall award the prize.

He claps his hands loudly and all the contestants enter from right and line up across the stage.

BARKER. As I hold my hand over the head of each group, indicate by your applause which contestants you liked best. (*He holds his hand over each group in turn. Audience applauds each, showing preference.*) Thank you. ——— (*names winning group*) are the winners. Here is the prize—tickets to the circus.

He takes the tickets from his pocket and gives one to each member of the winning group as the curtain falls.

QUEER QUARTETS
(*Short musical stunts*)

DOUBLE QUARTET.—Four girls, who are very good singers, make their hair very fluffy in front and attach boys' false faces to the backs of their heads. They wear boys' white slacks, put on backward, and plain white blouses, long-sleeved, high-necked, and fastening in the back. The blouses have collars, and neckties, invisible from the front, are tied in a loose knot in the back and fall down to the waist. Bright-colored sashes, with no bows, are tied around the girls' waists. Slacks should be long enough to hide the feet. The girls sidestep on the stage at left and sing any popular song, waving hands about and doing dance steps in place. When the song is finished, after the applause, the singers turn around, showing their boys' faces to the audience, wave their hands behind them, and sing another song. Then they sidestep offstage as they entered.

COMIC QUARTET.—Each member of the quartet should be dressed in the most absurd fashion possible, such as: bathing suit, silk top hat, and riding boots for one man; for the other man, blue overalls, tuxedo, bedroom slippers, and a helmet. For one woman, house dress, picture hat, and ballet slippers. For the second woman, ball gown, rubber boots, and sunbonnet. They should sing an operatic selection.

KIDDIES' QUARTET.—Four very large people, dressed as four very young children, sing some very old songs.

QUAVERING QUARTET.—Four young people dressed in old-style costumes, with white hair, wrinkles, canes, etc., sing, in cracked and quavering voices, modern songs.

THE HOME TOWN BAND
(*A kitchen band stunt*)

The name of the band should be lettered on two huge placards placed at opposite sides of the stage and on a third placard high up on the backdrop. The following names are suggested: Whatta Band, Frankly Goofy Band, Simpphoney Band.

Either piano accompaniment or off-stage records may be used for all the tunes. The following music is suitable: "Missouri Waltz," "Melody in F," "The Muffin Man," "Little Gray Home in the West," "Ol' Man River," "Bridal Chorus from Lohengrin," and as an encore, "Turkey in the Straw."

Costumes are simple. The director wears a dark blue suit with gilt braid in the coat. The male members of the band wear dark blue trousers, white shirts, and flowing red ties. The women wear long dark blue skirts, white blouses, and red belts.

When the curtain rises, the musicians are already in their seats on the stage, smiling happily. Back of the players with instruments are a group of men and women who can hum loudly and tunefully. Each has a kazoo— a small tin object on which anyone can play by simply humming through it. These kazoo players make the music, while those in front pantomime vigorously. The director stands in front and leads wildly, with a rolling-pin or a lead pipe for a baton.

The musicians may carry toy instruments, obtainable at any toy store, but the homemade instruments are much funnier. The following utensils may be used as instruments.

Cymbals—Two tin pot covers, clashed at appropriate moments in music

Banjo—A frying pan with cords stretched across it

Violin—A small shovel or trowel, with heavy twine strings, and a short curtain rod for a bow

Bass drum—A small tub or bucket, beaten with a dish mop

Bass viol—A long clothes basket with a short broomstick pushed through the handles and played with a long curtain rod or cane

Snare drum—A tin pan and cover

Kettledrum—A black kettle beaten with a mixing spoon

Cornet—A long funnel attached to a short piece of hose with a stick pushed through hose to keep it stiff

Fife—A cardboard mailing tube

Saxophone—A curtain rod attached to a large funnel, with a few clothespins snapped on in appropriate places; or a toy telephone with paper sacks fastened to it

Bells—Cowbells, sleighbells, or any other kind of bells

Bagpipes—Small gunny sacks attached to pieces of pipe

Castanets—The clackers often used at Halloween

Harp—A frame of beaverboard, gilded and strung with yellow cord

Bugle—A cardboard tube with a paper funnel at front

The kettledrum, castanets, bells, and cymbals actually make a noise when indicated by director at the most inappropriate places. While the kazoo players make the music, the other performers play with wildly exaggerated motions upon their instruments, watching the director with anxious attention. At the end of the program, all bow low to the audience and play an encore.

Other instruments may be added as desired. The worse they look, the more comical the effect.

THE MIGHTY MERLIN
(*A hypnotic stunt*)

The only properties necessary for this stunt are a dark curtain for a backdrop and an armchair on casters with wires attached to it and leading into the wings. The characters are Merlin and his assistant, Elaine. No accomplices are necessary. The audience will provide whatever suggestions are needed.

The curtain rises on a stage bare except for the armchair at center. MERLIN *enters from the left wing, dressed in a black robe and turban. He advances down center and addresses the audience gravely.*

MERLIN. Ladies and gentlemen, a great pleasure is in store for you. You are about to see me, myself in person, the Mighty Merlin, the greatest hypnotist in the world, living or dead. (*Raises his hand.*) Don't interrupt me with applause, no matter how much I deserve it. I must hurry because I am due to give a performance at the U. N. banquet tonight, when I hope to put even the Russian delegates into an amiable frame of mind, or perchance saw them in two. Now, will someone in the audience, anyone at all, please come up on the stage and be hypnotized? (*Someone volunteers.*) Thank you. Just sit in this chair. That's it. Lean back and be comfortable. Fold your arms. Extend your feet as far as possible. That's right. Now throw back your head—far back. Rest it against the back of this easy chair. Now you are perfectly comfortable, are you not? Relax! (MERLIN *places his forefinger gently on the victim's forehead and holds it there. He should have practiced on other people frequently enough*

to be able to find the right spot without difficulty.)
Now, my friend, you are hypnotized. You are helpless.
You cannot rise, no matter how hard you try. You
cannot rise until I give you permission. (*The victim
will strain and try to rise, but he really cannot, because
he must move his head forward in order to rise. The
steady pressure of* MERLIN's *forefinger on his forehead
prevents his rising.* MERLIN *lets him struggle for a
while. When he gives up,* MERLIN *speaks.*) Now, my
friend, I remove the spell. You are free to go. Rise.
(MERLIN *removes his forefinger and the victim staggers
off the stage.*) And now, ladies and gentlemen, I shall
send my assistant out of the room— Oh, she hasn't been
in yet. Has she? Elaine, come here.

ELAINE, *a pretty girl in white, enters at left.*

ELAINE. Yes, Merlin?
MERLIN (*to audience*). Elaine will be hypnotized by
me, and you shall decide what she is to do. Elaine, leave
the stage. I will call you back when I am ready.
ELAINE. Yes, Merlin. (*Exit at left.*)
MERLIN. Now, friends, give me your command.
What shall I have Elaine do? Speak softly so she can-
not hear.

The audience will usually suggest a lot of silly ideas.
This is not planned ahead and Merlin will have to take
one of the suggestions. Naturally he will select a simple
one, also one that is easy to spell. If he repeats this
one a number of times, the others in the audience will
gradually decide they like that suggestion, also. Let us
suppose the audience agrees that Elaine is to dance and
to sing "Sweet Adeline." See "You're the Flower of
My Heart" in the music in the back of the book.

MERLIN. Very well. Elaine shall dance, and she shall
sing "Sweet Adeline." (*He calls.*) Elaine.

ELAINE *enters at left.*

MERLIN. Sit down, Elaine. (*She sits in the arm-
chair facing audience. MERLIN stands back of chair.*)
ELAINE. Yes, Merlin.
MERLIN (*stroking her forehead gently*). You are
tired. Your eyelids are heavy. Shut your eyes, Elaine.
ELAINE (*drowsily*). Yes, Merlin. (*Shuts her eyes.*)
MERLIN (*stroking her forehead*). Now you are
asleep, Elaine. Think. Think well, while I stroke your
weary head. Soon you will know what you are to do.
Think, Elaine. Obey the will of the great Merlin.

(*He strokes her forehead, then stops for a moment
and stands, looking down at her. Then he begins stroking again, and this time his strokes convey the message.
Each stroke or series of strokes is followed by a slight
pause. Each stroke or series of strokes represents a
letter of the alphabet and helps spell the direction. A
is one stroke; b is two, c is three, etc. This sounds as
if spelling a word would be an interminable process but
it really is not. If the command, "Dance" is given,
MERLIN would deliver the order as follows: four strokes,
pause; one stroke, pause; fourteen strokes, pause; three
strokes, pause; five strokes, pause. ELAINE must give
the strokes her undivided attention. If she does not
respond promptly, MERLIN repeats the directions.*)

ELAINE (*rising slowly from chair*). Dance. I must
dance. (*To the music of "Sweet Adeline." She waltzes
or tap-dances about the room, and then sinks, still pre-
tending to be asleep, into the chair.*)

(*Another order or two may be carried out, and then* MERLIN *ends the show.*)

MERLIN. Wake, Elaine. Wake, my child. (*He strokes her forehead gently again and she stirs, opens her eyes, looks about her blankly. She turns the chair so it faces left, as if not wishing to see the audience.* MERLIN *speaks to the audience.*) You have seen the power of the great Merlin. And now, my friends, it is time to conclude our performance. I shall put Elaine to sleep again and blow her off the stage. Close your eyes, Elaine. (ELAINE *again closes her eyes.* MERLIN *strokes her forehead again.*) Leave the stage, Elaine, and awake in your dressing room.

(*He puffs at the back of the chair, and someone in the wings pulls it off by the wires attached to it. The chair is on casters and disappears rapidly.* MERLIN *bows low to the audience, and—*)

THE CURTAIN FALLS

WHAT DO YOU SEE IN MUSIC?
(*Short musical pantomimes*)

The stage should be set with an easel down extreme left and beside it a number of large cards, each bearing the name of a different song to be played and portrayed. A small boy from the wings or the Announcer, who stands down left throughout the performance, may change the cards at the close of each pantomime. The pantomimes may be presented on the bare stage, with only a dark cyclorama as a background. To allow time for changing settings, the order of the pantomimes should be so arranged that one requiring only a few properties alternates with a pantomime with a more elaborate setting. If the stage has a drop curtain, one scene may be arranged behind it while another is being played before the main curtain.

The music for the pantomimes may be presented on records, played on a piano, or, as in the case of the vocal music, sung by a chorus seated just below the stage. The music of every selection portrayed by the pantomime should be played throughout the entire pantomime.

Before the first pantomime is shown, the Announcer enters down left and addresses the audience.

ANNOUNCER. Friends, did you ever stop to think— Now that's a foolish question. Of course you didn't. Never mind. I'll tell you. Whenever you hear a familiar piece of music—a composition of which you are very fond, or even one that you do not like—your mind's eye instantly sees a picture. A different picture for each of us, no doubt, but a picture. Permit me to show you what I mean. While the following music is played or sung, these are the pictures that appear in *my* imagination.

He places the card that gives the title of the first pantomime on the easel, and the music of the selection starts offstage. The curtain rises on the first pantomime.

HOME ON THE RANGE.—The scene is a kitchen. At center is an old rusty stove covered with pots, pans, etc. At left is a table set for a large family. A tired, bedraggled woman wearing a huge apron stands beside the stove stirring the contents of pots and pans, looking in the oven, and every minute glancing anxiously at the huge clock on the table. She wipes her brow with her apron, sniffs as she smells something burning, and takes one pot off the stove. From right a large family enters—a man and many children of assorted sizes. They sit at the table and pound on plates with knives, being annoyed because the meal is not ready. The woman glares at them and bangs the pots on the table in front of them as she takes them off the stove, while the curtain falls.

THE LOST CHORD.—No setting is needed except a table, upon which is a huge package a man is trying to prepare for mailing. He folds the paper covering carefully, licks and pastes on the parcel post sticker and reaches for the ball of cord. It isn't on the table. He looks in the table drawer and finds a few short pieces of string. He ties them together and finds they are too short to reach around the package. He looks frantically for the ball of cord on the floor and under the small rug before the table. He takes out the contents of the table drawer and dumps it on the floor.

There is much assorted junk but no cord. He turns his pockets inside out, lifts the package, feels of it, discovers a lump, removes his careful wrappings, and finds the ball of cord in the package. He restrains his rage with difficulty and starts to rewrap the package as the curtain falls.

SCHOOL DAYS.—Scene is a small schoolroom, with a movable blackboard at the back and near it the teacher's desk, which faces the audience. On the desk is a small bell. Children of assorted sizes are at their desks in two rows facing right. The teacher, a stern-faced female, sits at her desk. On the blackboard may be written a few rather absurd questions. Children are busily writing in perfect silence. She taps the bell. They quietly put their papers away and sit erect with their hands folded on the desks. The teacher hears a noise in the hall and goes off at left. At once the pupils become riotous. One draws a picture on the blackboard and labels it "Teacher." Others spar, tap-dance, whistle, and chase one another around the room. The teacher returns, stands at left, and glares. The pupils rush to their seats, fold their hands, face front, and all is silence as the curtain falls.

TWINKLE, TWINKLE, LITTLE STAR.—The curtain rises on an empty stage. A small child who dances well enters and does a dance to the music of the song. Then she runs offstage.

SOMEWHERE A VOICE IS CALLING.—On an empty stage a boy is reading a comic book happily. A little girl is playing with her doll. Suddenly, from offstage, a shrill voice calls, "Children, come home this minute."

The two pick up their belongings and reluctantly go off at left.

OVERTURE TO "WILLIAM TELL."—Curtain rises showing two men, one in a brown doublet and hose, with a bow and arrow, the other in a blue suit trimmed with gold braid, wearing a helmet of gilt paper, a sword at his side. A small boy dressed like the first man has a huge red apple on his head. Gessler is urging the father to shoot the apple off the boy's head. Father goes up to the son, removes the apple, and motions to the boy to run away, and he darts off at right. Tell places the apple upon his own head and dares Gessler to shoot it off, giving him his bow and arrow. Gessler accepts the challenge and draws careful aim. Tell removes the apple from his head and takes a huge bite. Gessler angrily orders Tell to put the apple back on his head and aims again. Tell takes a bite from the apple. This is repeated, with increasingly violent gestures, until the apple is eaten up. Tell throws the core at Gessler and runs off at right, pursued by Gessler, who throws down his bow and arrow and draws his sword, as the curtain falls.

GOLLIWOG'S CAKE WALK.—As the curtain rises, any number of boys do an eccentric, jerky dance to music. They wear bright green caps, long red trousers, white shoes, white belts or sashes, and enormous goggles.

ANVIL CHORUS.—Four women are seated at a bridge table. They start to bid. One remembers a choice bit of gossip and repeats it. All join very heartily in criticizing an absent friend. One of the four leaves the room, and the remaining three take her apart. When she returns, they all resume their former topic of gossip, pounding the table and shaking their heads. As the conversation grows violent, the curtain falls.

INDIAN LOVE CALL.—As the curtain rises, any number of Indians in blankets and feather headdresses are hopping around in a circle, the center of which is a camp fire. It is made of small sticks, red and yellow crepe paper flames, and electric bulbs or flashlights under the sticks to represent coals. The dancers change the direction of the circle several times, then form a line and face left. Putting their hands up to their mouths, they give a blood-curdling war whoop, as the curtain falls.

WHEN THE MOON COMES OVER THE MOUNTAIN.—The backdrop is made of beaverboard or paper stretched on a wooden frame and painted to represent a dark sky. In front of it stand large beaverboard mountains. Just behind the mountains stands a short adult or a child carrying a big round yellow pasteboard moon attached to a stiff wire invisible to the audience. The person holding the wire tries to raise it above the mountain against the sky. The moon comes up with great difficulty. It shows a fraction of an inch at first, then slips down, tries again, and rises slowly, then spasmodically. At last it makes it with a dash, as the curtain falls.

GIVE ME SOMETHING TO REMEMBER YOU BY.—A girl stands by a table, upon which are piled jewel boxes, candy and flower boxes, etc. She fingers a string of pearls about her neck, also bracelets on her wrists and rings on her fingers, but appears dissatisfied. Books and a small radio are also on the table. A young man

enters with a suitcase, to bid her good-bye. She extends
her hand for a parting gift. He looks dismayed, points
to the table and the jewelry, and shakes his head. She
grows angry and shakes her forefinger at him. He sadly
puts down the suitcase and exits hurriedly. She re-
arranges the gifts on the table and fingers the jewelry
as before. He returns with a fur coat. She joyously
puts it on and bids him an affectionate farewell, as the
curtain falls.

KEEP THE HOME FIRES BURNING.—Against the backdrop stands a huge ·thermometer, with a thermostat
hanging on the wall near it. On a small table at center
is a pitcher filled with ice. A sink, made of cardboard,
stands beside the table. Large pencils covered with
silver paper may be used as faucets. A man enters,
wearing an overcoat, galoshes, earmuffs, and a scarf
around his throat. He looks at the thermometer and
is shocked. He looks at the thermostat and tries to
turn it up. It is frozen and will not move. He goes to
the sink and tries the faucets. They come off in his
hands, frozen. He turns the pitcher upside down, and
the ice falls out. He slaps his arms around his body
to get warm, as the curtain falls.

YOU FORGOT TO REMEMBER.—The scene is a living
room. The back wall should be made with gaily painted
screens. On one screen is fastened a large calendar.
Nearby is a sofa, on which sits a fussily dressed woman.
She keeps looking impatiently at her wrist watch. Her
husband returns from work. She rushes to greet him
and looks at him expectantly. He calmly removes his
coat, and she at once feels in the pockets and finds nothing. He hands her the evening paper, which she

angrily throws on the floor. He asks what the trouble is, and she points to the calendar. It is her birthday. He looks ashamed. She has hysterics as the curtain falls.

As TIME GOES BY, or, DANCE OF THE HOURS.—With measured tread, twelve girls enter from right, stepping sidewise. Each girl wears two immense cardboard clock faces hanging around her neck, one in front and the other behind. Each girl's clock faces show a different hour, and the hours range from one to twelve. The hands are very large and black, so as to be easily seen by the audience. If the first musical number is used, the girls march slowly and deliberately around the stage and back again. If the second number is used, they do a dignified dance and then leave the stage.

SMILES.—Any number of men and women, dressed in eccentric clothing ranging from very stylish garments to rags, enter at right, stand in a line across the front of the stage and smile. Smiles are painted heavily on their faces and are as varied as possible—thin-lipped, broad grins, sinister leers, toothless smiles, coy ones, etc.

AMARYLLIS.—Any number of girls skip on the stage dressed as fairies in short ruffled skirts and tight, sleeveless, waists of pastel shades of mosquito netting, dyed the color desired, socks to match and white slippers. They do a dainty dance, then skip off the stage.

ANNOUNCER (*removing sign*). See what I mean?

CURTAIN

MR. TOTTEN TAKES A REST
(*A reading with sound effects*)

Each guest at the party is given a slip of paper, on which is written the name of the animal he or she is to imitate. It should be made clear to all that every time the name on the paper is mentioned in the story, the holder of the paper must make the sound of the animal—or plant—loudly and promptly. This story calls for the following animals and plants: any number of crickets, at least four frogs, two cows, two sheep, two cats, any number of dogs, one rooster, one owl, a group of buds, a convenient number of toads, and the same of fish. The toads' business is to hop up and down six times in succession. The sound of fish swimming is imitated by pouring water from one pail to another; or the fish may just say, "splash!" The sound of buds bursting is made by sticking pins into small inflated balloons. The hostess should have the pails of water and the balloons ready when the game starts.

The narrator should pause briefly after pronouncing the name of each animal in order to give the players a chance to imitate the sound of their respective animals.

Just before the narrator begins to read the story, a pianist plays Grainger's "Country Gardens."

NARRATOR.

Have you ever gone to the country for a rest and come home without it? If so, you will sympathize with Mr. Totten whose sad story I am about to relate.

Mr. Totten was very tired. He worked in the noisy city in a noisy office, surrounded by noisy typists and noisy stenographers. Mr. Totten grew more nervous every day. He couldn't conceal it any longer. He jumped every time the office boy popped his bubble gum.

He jumped every time there was a traffic jam down the
street and the whistles blew and the horns tooted. He
jumped every time the elevator door slammed. In short,
Mr. Totten was jumpy.

So he determined to take a rest and get away from
it all. He realized he needed a vacation in a quiet,
peaceful spot, and he knew just were to find that quiet,
peaceful spot: on his uncle Jed's farm, down in the
country. Uncle Jed's farm was miles away from a village. It was miles away from a railroad; in fact, it
was miles away from a road. There Mr. Totten could
take a rest—a well-earned rest. So there Mr. Totten
went.

Uncle Jed was sound asleep at eight o'clock, and the
rural peace and quiet of evening belonged to Mr. Totten
alone. He settled himself on the porch to enjoy it. At
last he could rest. On one side of the house was a cool
green wood. On the other side was a pretty little pond.
Back of the house was a meadow where Uncle Jed's two
cows lived, also his two sheep. In front of the house
was a flower garden. What a perfect place! Mr.
Totten closed his eyes blissfully.

Then suddenly the frogs in the pond began their
evening concert. Their tune was answered by the
crickets in the meadow. Poor Mr. Totten jumped and
for a moment thought he must be dreaming of the city
and its weird noises. From the woods an owl asked a
question over and over, but no one answered. Then,
the noise subsided. The quiet was so intense it hurt Mr.
Totten's ears. But not for long. The quiet was broken
by a gentle popping sound in the garden. The buds
were bursting into bloom. They had evidently mistaken
the glowing moonlight for the rays of the morning sun.
From the meadow came the insistent moos of the cows,
as if they were having nightmares. The moos aroused

the sheep, and their baas filled the air with plaintive reproaches.

Then once again all was still, so still that Mr. Totten could hear the toads hopping in the garden and the gentle splashing of the fish in the pond. Mr. Totten could have rested, listening to the fish, but he never knew when the other sounds would begin again. It was like waiting for the guy who slept next door to drop his other shoe.

In the distance a dog began to bark. He was answered by a dog nearer by, by another still nearer, and then another. Uncle Jed's Rover joined in, and it was a very mournful chorus. Tabby and Tommy, the cats, evidently thought so, too, for they began a shrill protest; and when Tabby and Tommy protested—they protested. The others became exhausted and stopped, but Rover and Tommy sang a duet for some time. At last they wore themselves out and stopped for breath.

Then the frogs began to sing once more. The crickets answered, the cows lamented, the sheep complained, the buds burst louder and faster than before, the owl hooted loudly, the toads hopped, the fish splashed, Rover barked, and Tommy meowed. Then they all joined in, their voices became one mighty chorus—an anthem to the night.

Poor Mr. Totten gnashed his teeth and tore his hair. Finally the noise became less and less. One by one, the sounds died away. The frogs, the crickets, the owl, the cows, the sheep, the dogs, the cats, all became silent. There was only the bursting of the buds in the garden, the toads hopping, and the fish splashing in the pond. One by one, they, too, died away, until, with a last faint ripple from the pond, all was silent. The countryside was sleeping. Mr. Totten, exhausted, slept, too, in his

chair on the porch.   At last he could rest.   Moments
went by—at least ten of them.   (*A pause.*)

From the barn came a clarion call.   Uncle Jed's
rooster thought it was morning and time for him to
wake up the sun.   He crowed long and lustily.   In so
doing, he awoke the echoes, also everything else that was
sleeping, within a radius of five miles.   (*All noises begin
and then stop abruptly.*)

The next morning Mr. Totten went back to his noisy
office in the noisy city.   By comparison, it seemed quiet.
In a few days he felt quite rested.

(*"The Sidewalks of New York" is played by the
pianist or by a record.*)

COURTSHIP THROUGH THE AGES
(*Four pantomimes with music*)

NARRATOR (*coming before the curtain and addressing the audience*). It's love that makes the world go round, they say. Let's take a look at the various styles of love-making through the ages. Now in prehistoric times— (*He takes his place down extreme right.*)

SCENE 1

The curtain rises, showing a row of ragged green bushes against a dark cyclorama. At the center of the stage is a fire, made of sticks and red crêpe paper, with flashlights beneath them to represent flames. Rocks are scattered about the stage. On one, back of the fire, sits a cave man in a costume of flesh-colored tights and a leopard skin. His hair is long and red. His face is brown and fierce. He holds a club with a massive knot on the end. A cave woman, also in tights and a plain black skin, made from an old fur coat, peeps at him from behind the bushes. Her black hair hangs over her eyes. He spies her and rises. She starts to run across the stage. He catches her, conks her over the head with his club, swings her over his shoulder and carries her, kicking wildly, offstage. During this scene the music is "The Storm" from "William Tell."

CURTAIN

NARRATOR. In days of the Pilgrims and the Puritans—

SCENE 2

The curtain rises to the music of the "Pilgrims'

Chorus" from "Tannhauser." A young man in Puritan dress meets a girl in Puritan dress. The stage is absolutely empty. They look cautiously about as if fearing an Indian attack. They approach each other bashfully. He asks a question. She nods timidly. He kisses her respectfully on the brow and takes her hand, and they stroll offstage.

CURTAIN

NARRATOR. From Civil War time, up to, and including the so-called gay nineties—

SCENE 3

To the music of "Love's Old Sweet Song" or "I Love You Truly," the curtain rises on a bare stage set with a few chairs. A young man in the costume of the Civil War period or the gay nineties, according to preference, is interviewing the father, who is stern and asks many questions in pantomime, with wide gestures. He calls in the mother, who also asks questions. The young man wipes the perspiration from his brow and grows limp from exhaustion and anxiety. At last the girl is called in. The parents reluctantly leave the room, while the young people stand and wait for them to go. The lovers then rush into each other's arms. The parents return and stare at them. All costumes should be of the same period.

CURTAIN

NARRATOR. And today— (*Whistles.*)

SCENE 4

To the music of "Can't Help Lovin' That Man" from "The Showboat," the curtain rises on a living room. A mother and father are sitting on a sofa. A young man, wearing slacks and sweater, enters and greets them carelessly. They rise and leave the room. The young man whistles. A girl in slacks and sweater rushes in, literally throws herelf at the young man, kisses him soundly, and holds out her left hand to him as if expecting him to slip a diamond on it. He looks embarrassed, for he hasn't brought any diamond along. She shows him a calendar, which is lying on the sofa, points to a date in the following week, and speaks sternly. He protests, "no money" and shows an empty billfold and only a few coins. She insists. At last he agrees meekly. She calls in her parents and announces her engagement. They assent hopelessly, and the young man staggers out, presumably to buy the ring. While the parents are trying to recover from the shock, he returns, carrying a a few chairs. A young man in the costume of the Civil War period or the gay nineties, according to preference, is interviewing the father, who is stern and asks many questions in pantomime, with wide gestures. He calls in the mother, who also asks questions. The young man wipes the perspiration from his brow and grows limp from exhaustion and anxiety. At last the girl is called in. The parents reluctantly leave the room, while the young people stand and wait for them to go. The lovers then rush into each other's arms. The parents return and stare at them. All costumes should be of the same period.

CURTAIN

NARRATOR. And today— (*Whistles.*)

SCENE 4

To the music of "Can't Help Lovin' That Man" from "The Showboat," the curtain rises on a living room. A mother and father are sitting on a sofa. A young man, wearing slacks and sweater, enters and greets them carelessly. They rise and leave the room. The young man whistles. A girl in slacks and sweater rushes in, literally throws herelf at the young man, kisses him soundly, and holds out her left hand to him as if expecting him to slip a diamond on it. He looks embarrassed, for he hasn't brought any diamond along. She shows him a calendar, which is lying on the sofa, points to a date in the following week, and speaks sternly. He protests, "no money" and shows an empty billfold and only a few coins. She insists. At last he agrees meekly. She calls in her parents and announces her engagement. They assent hopelessly, and the young man staggers out, presumably to buy the ring. While the parents are trying to recover from the shock, he returns, carrying a ring with an enormous stone. As he slips it on the girl's finger, the music changes to that of a wedding march.

Narrator bows to the audience and exits.

CURTAIN

THE TRAVELOGUE OF PHINEAS FLOGG
(*A geographical pantomime*)

FLOGG *comes before the curtain and addresses the audience.*

FLOGG. I, Phineas Flogg, have traveled everywhere and met many interesting and unusual people. I am not going to bore you with reels of movies and reams of eloquence. I am going to show you in a very few minutes what pleased me most in certain places I visited. You'll have to go there yourselves to see what you like best. (*Takes his place down extreme right, where he remains throughout the performance.*)

SCENE 1

The curtain rises to the music of "Killarney." At the back of the stage sit two elderly men in Irish peasant costumes, smoking long clay pipes. Irish girls in green and white dresses enter and sing a group of old Irish songs, such as "Believe Me, if All Those Endearing Young Charms," "Come Back to Erin," etc., and go off. Then the music becomes an Irish jig and the leprechauns enter. These are small boys in tight green trousers and blouses, little round green caps, and white shoes. They do a wild jig.

CURTAIN

FLOGG. You've guessed it. Ireland. From there I went to Scotland, land of the kilt and the bagpipe.

SCENE 2

To the music of "The Campbells are Comin'," the

curtain rises on a group of boys and girls in Scotch costume, wearing bright braids. They dance a Highland fling. Then the same group, or another in similar costumes, sing Scotch songs, such as "Annie Laurie," "Bluebells of Scotland," "Bonnie Doon," etc. If possible end the scene by having a bagpipe record played offstage. Those on stage look off in the direction of the music and advance to meet the players as—

THE CURTAIN FALLS

FLOGG. Come with me to Holland. Windmills and tulips everywhere! We will go to the island of Maarken.

SCENE 3

When the curtain rises to the music of "The Dutch Warbler," the stage is set with many rows of bright-colored paper tulips at the sides and several large beaverboard windmills at the back. If windmills are hard to obtain, the children may represent them, standing back to back, with arms raised and revolving like windmill arms. The children work their arms rhythmically throughout the entire scene. They wear Dutch costumes, with wooden shoes made of yellow cloth or paper, pasted over old slippers or rubbers. Many people in Dutch costumes stroll by. A group of children do a clog dance to the tune of "The Dutch Warbler."

CURTAIN

FLOGG. The next summer I journeyed to China. I found the Chinese children playing their favorite game, which they call "grinding coffee." You shall see it.

SCENE 4

The curtain rises to the music of "Chinese Dance"

from "The Nutcracker Suite" by Tchaikovsky. On the stage are as many children as desired, in Chinese costume, long black trousers, and long, bright-colored blouses, their dark hair smooth. They stand in two rows, lengthwise across the stage, partners facing each other. Their hands are clasped in front. The two ends of each line come together, thus forming two concentric circles, partners facing each other as before. One pair of arms is raised, the boy's left arm and the girl's right, and the couple turn under their arms to one side and thus arrive back to back, dropping their arms down at their sides. Then the other pair of arms is raised and turned in the same manner so the couple arrive at their first position, facing each other. It is the familiar movement found in many children's games when one partner turns under the other's arm. In this game, both partners turn. All couples do this at once and as rapidly as possible. The motion is continuous, and the curtain must fall before the players become exhausted and slow down their action.

CURTAIN

FLOGG. Last of all, to Mexico, land of music and flowers, bullfights and ballads, fiestas and frijoles. You shall see the famous toreador, Tony, and the brave bull, Clarence.

SCENE 5

The curtain rises to the music of "La Paloma." The stage is set as if for a bullfight. At the back and at the sides, seated on camp chairs, are men, women, and children in bright clothing, with serapes, rebozos, and sombreros. Flower vendors are carrying baskets of bright-colored paper flowers. A mixed chorus comes down to the front and sings a group of Mexican songs, including "La Paloma." From offstage comes the sound of a trumpet. The music changes to "The Toreador's Song," from "Carmen." Tony the Toreador, in gorgeous costume, enters from right and the crowd applauds. Then, from left Clarence the Bull prances in. Clarence is played by a large young man in black costume. His hands and feet are covered with yellow to represent hoofs. His suit is cut over a one-piece sleeping suit pattern, and the yellow hoofs are attached. The head is covered with a black hood to which are attached long wicked looking yellow horns and black ears. The tail is long and very bushy at the end. Clarence walks on his hind legs. He bellows loudly as he enters, the sound being made by a trumpet player offstage. Tony takes his red cape from his shoulders and waves it. Clarence grows angry. They have a mock fight, being as funny as possible, and then Clarence grows tired and gentle. He throws his arms around Tony and they dance. The audience wants a fight, so all the people hiss and motion to them to continue the hostilities. Clarence nods assent. Tony again waves his cape. Clarence knocks Tony down and stands with one foot on his stomach. The audience applauds wildly. Flower vendors throw flowers at Clarence, who picks up a red rose, smells it, and puts it behind his ear. He bows low to both audiences—the one on stage and the one before him. He strikes a noble attitude, one foot still on Tony's stomach.

Curtain

Flogg. And now we leave colorful, magic Mexico, for the busy world of the U. S. A. *Hasta la vista* and *adios*, amigos. (*Exit.*)

THE CALENDAR
(*A musical pantomime*)

ANNOUNCER (*coming before the curtain*). A friend of mine had a horrible dream last night. I want to tell you about it, as an awful warning not to take your work too seriously. This friend—Chloe is her name—not the one that is lost in the swamp, though there are times when *she'd* like to be. This Chloe is an artist, a commercial artist, but still—an artist. Her life work is designing beautiful calendars. You know the kind—very arty, very, very arty, with appropriate scenes and stuff. Well, Chloe is a very conscientious creature, and she works very hard all the time. Last night she went to bed early to get a good night's rest, and what happened? All night long she dreamed. Her calendar pictures came to life, and she saw them all night long. She's a wreck today. And all because she takes her work too seriously. I'll tell you about her dream. (*Exits at left.*)

The curtain rises on an empty stage to the music of the "Dance of the Hours" from "La Gioconda." Immediately the groups representing each month in the year enter, one by one, at right, parade or dance across the stage and go off at left.

JANUARY.—From offstage come the sounds of bells and horns, mingling with the music. A gay crowd of men and women in evening dress enter at right and begin to dance. A clock offstage strikes twelve very loudly. Everybody kisses everybody else, and all dance off at left.

FEBRUARY.—To the music of Boccherini's "Minuet," a group of young men and women in colonial costume enter at right and dance a graceful minuet. As soon as they go off at left, a group of girls in white dresses with red hearts on their heads parade across the stage from right to left to the music of "Sweet Adeline." They go off at left.

MARCH.—To the music of "Killarney," a group of girls in Irish costumes dance on stage and sing a group of Irish songs, ending with a jig danced to the music of "The Wearing of the Green." Then they dance off-stage.

APRIL.—While the music of "The Dance of the Comedians" by Smetana is played, a group of clowns, wearing extravagantly silly suits and make-up, false noses, etc., enter and do an acrobatic dance. At the end, they burst into tears, wiping their eyes on enormous red handkerchiefs and running off at left.

MAY.—To the music of Mendelssohn's "Spring Song," two boys enter, carrying a Maypole in a standard, with pink, blue, green, and yellow streamers. They set it in the middle of the stage and exeunt. Immediately a group of girls and boys enter in summer costumes, each takes a streamer, and they dance a Maypole dance, winding the ribbons around the pole.

JUNE.—To the music of the Bridal Chorus from "Lohengrin," a bridal party enters and parades across the stage. There are at least six bridesmaids wearing gowns in pastel shades and large picture hats. The bride wears an elaborate white bridal gown, and the groom and his attendants wear the conventional black.

JULY.—A mixed or male quartet, wearing white suits and red-white-and-blue caps, enter to the music of the "Liberty Bell March," and sing "Battle Hymn of the Republic" and other patriotic songs.

AUGUST.—To the music of "Over the Waves," a

group of girls in bathing suits saunter on the stage at right, cross it, and go off left.

SEPTEMBER.—To the music of "School Days" or "The Prisoner's Song," a number of children carrying bags of schoolbooks enter at left just as half a dozen tanned men and women carrying suitcases enter at right. The children on their way to school and the adults returning from vacations pass each other at center, the former going off at right and the latter at left.

OCTOBER.—While Saint-Saëns' "Danse Macabre" is played, ghosts and goblins, witches carrying their broomsticks, and big black cats cross the stage in a Halloween parade. The ghosts and goblins may do a weird dance.

NOVEMBER.—To the music of "Over the River and Through the Woods," a choir in black robes and caps enter, and sing "Come, Ye Thankful People, Come" and any doxology.

DECEMBER.—As the entrance music, "Santa Claus is Comin' to Town," is played, Santa Claus enters at left, wearing the customary red suit. His reindeer and sleigh, which are cut out of brown cardboard, are pushed on the stage at left by small boys, who, being smaller than the reindeer and sleigh, will not be visible to the audience. Brownies in brown suits and red caps enter at left, dance around Santa, then sing old or modern Christmas songs. The boys behind the reindeer push them offstage at the end.

When the December players have left the stage, the Announcer enters down left and addresses the audience.

ANNOUNCER. It may not have seemed so terrible to you, but Chloe didn't want those people around night and day. Would you? (*Exit.*)

DAME DIMWITTY'S DOLLS
(*A pantomime with dancing*)

Dame Dimwitty is an elderly woman with a decidedly daffy expression. She looks as if she had found her clothes is an old trunk in the attic. Her dolls, at least twelve in number, are seated in chairs across the stage toward the back, leaving sufficient room in front of the chairs for the dancing.

The dolls are as weird in appearance as their owner. Faces are heavily made up, hair dressed in every imaginable style, from crew cut to long curls and pompadour. The dolls are dressed in as incongruous and amazing garments as rompers, Mother Hubbards, ball gowns, bathing suits, Eskimo coats and hoods, etc. They sit motionless, erect and stiff in their chairs.

Dame Dimwitty enters, goes back of the chairs, and, with a "clacker" winds up the dolls. As each doll is wound up, she rises and stands stiffly. When all are standing, music from piano or record offstage is heard, and the dolls dance. The first selection is "De Camptown Races," and all are gay and peppy. The second selection is "Narcissus," by Nevin.

Halfway through their dance to this tune, the dolls begin to run down. The music becomes slow and faltering, as does the dance. The dolls move more and more slowly. Those first wound up slow down first. Dame Dimwitty manages to steer each doll into her chair before she collapses. As the last doll sits, the music ceases with a whirring sound. The dolls sit as before. Dame Dimwitty stands behind them, as the curtain falls.

THE STYLES OF OTHER DAYS
(*A fashion parade*)

Probably no stunt has been done, or overdone, more often than the fashion parade, but it is still popular. Directions for costumes are not needed. Look in your attic and go to the library and consult the fashion books of years past. Some of the ladies will wear long bell-skirts, tight basques with huge puffed sleeves, high buttoned shoes and hats ranging from plain sailors to floppy picture hats weighed down with flowers. Others will wear tight little turbans with flowing veils. Others will wear bustles or ruffled pantalets, which they take care to show by flirting their long skirts about. Styles for men during various periods of history may be found in books, also, but are not quite so mirth-provoking as the corresponding attire for women. Children's styles are easily obtainable in books.

A bare stage is shown, with the paraders entering at one side, crossing, and going off at the other side.

To the music of "Easter Parade," people in period costumes are seen going to church—a man and his wife, with two children, a boy and a girl. As many family groups as desired may parade.

The music changes to "A Bicycle Built for Two." A man and a woman enter riding a tandem bicycle or, if a tandem is unobtainable, a bicycle apiece. She wears a divided skirt, a tight jacket, cap with visor, blue goggles, heavy gloves, and high shoes. He wears a dark suit and derby hat. They ride across the stage and exeunt at the opposite side.

The music again changes to "A Bird in a Gilded Cage" or, if preferred, the "Beautiful Blue Danube Waltzes." A pretty girl dances on stage with a young

man.   He wears a dress suit of the period.   She wears
a very low-cut, off-shoulder pale blue dress with a train,
long white gloves, black slippers, a string of pearls
about her neck and her hair in a high pompadour that
makes her as tall as her partner.   She carries an ostrich
feather fan, and a dance program dangles from her
wrist.   She looks bored.

To the music of "Let's Take an Old-fashioned Walk,"
by Berlin, a young man and his sweetheart, in the costumes of the nineties, stroll across the stage, looking
very happy.   They may be followed by as many other
similar couples as desired.

As a finale, all the groups of paraders cross the stage
again in the order in which they first appeared while
the music of "Long, Long Ago" is played.

SHIPWRECK TODAY

or

Robinson Crusoe Up to Date

(*A burlesque stunt*)

The scene is a desert island. The floor is covered with yellow canvas to represent sand. The sounds of rushing waves and screaming seagulls are heard. The sound of rushing waves is produced by putting a handful of BB shot into a box covered with wire screening and tilting the box so that the shot will roll over the wire and make a swishing noise. The sound of screaming seagulls is simulated by drawing a resined string violently through a small hole in a tin can.

In the middle of the stage on the yellow cloth sits a man, barefooted and clothed in rags, a pack of dirty cards in his hands. He shakes his head and sighs loudly. Down right, propped up in the sand is a huge calendar, bearing a date of the past year in print large enough to be read by the audience. The man rises, goes to the calendar, tears off the page, and shows another page bearing a date of the current year. He sighs again and wipes his eyes. He yawns, puts his hand over his eyes, and scans the horizon. The sound of an explosion comes from offstage. It is made by shaking a piece of heavy tin or thin sheet iron in the wings, then dropping a heavy iron chain from the top of a pole upon a sheet of tin laid on the top of an empty ashcan, in imitation of a blast that blows the ship to fragments.

The man starts and looks about him again. Bits of splintered wood fly on the stage from right, being tossed from the wings. Spray spatters the sand, coming from a hose in the wings at right. Then all is silence. The

man is tragically disappointed. He sits, his head in his
hands. The sound of faint splashing is heard, gradually
growing louder and nearer. This sound is made by
slapping the surface of a tub of water with a paddle
off in the wings. At the sound, the man looks up. The
dripping figure of a man, wearing a life belt, enters at
right, coughs, and falls flat on his face in the sand.
Our hero rushes to him, raises his head, and says
eagerly, "Do you play canasta?"

Section Four

Pantomines and Charades

THE BALLAD OF REGINALD ROYCE

This verse is read or recited by one person and a chorus, seated at the back of the reader, who repeats certain lines after the reader, as indicated. The effect is that of an echo.

Reginald Royce loved a girl named Joyce
    Chorus: A girl named Joyce
And begged her to give him some hope,
But the gal named Joyce in her gentle voice
    Said "Poor Reggie, you're a dope."
    Chorus (*loudly*): You're a dope.
'Twas all very sad and he soon felt so bad
    He thought of a quick suicide.
    Chorus: A quick suicide.
Stuck his head in a noose but 'twas far too loose
    And the knot just wouldn't stay tied.
    Chorus (*sadly*): Just wouldn't stay tied.
He jumped from a cliff with his legs very stiff
    But landed in somebody's pool.
He then slashed his wrist but the blue veins he missed,
    Poor Reggie was such a sad fool.
    Chorus: Such a sad fool!
He never could swim so with vigor and vim
    He flung himself out of a boat
In a wild raging tide, his sorrow to hide,
    But all Reggie did was just float.
    Chorus: Just float.
So, to end it all he gulped down a tall
    Green glass filled with cold arsenic.
    Chorus: Cold arsenic.
It tasted right queer, but dear me, never fear.
    He wasn't a little bit sick.

Chorus: He wasn't a little bit sick.
He then aimed a gun, a big loaded one,
 Right at his poor broken heart.
It grazed his right knee, then passed through a tree,
 And gave the poor chap quite a start.
  Chorus: Quite a start.
He thought in vain how release he might gain
 From the sorrow that darkened his life.
There was nothing to do but just see the thing
   through,
 So he said, "Why should I want a wife?"
  Chorus (*disgustedly*): Want a wife!
"I'll forget what's-her-name,—was it Ruth or Elaine?
 And just be a man about town."
  Chorus: A man about town.
So he did and he is, he's a regular whiz.
 The moral? Don't let love get you down.
  Chorus: Don't let love get you down.

RED RIDING HOOD UP TO DATE

Some one reads the following story with sound effects and music coming from behind a screen or at the extreme right of the room.

Music (*piano*). "Stars of the Summer Night."

READER. It was a lovely summer evening. The wind sighed softly through the trees. (*Loud swishing sound by rattling a piece of tin or turning an electric fan on loose pieces of paper.*) The birds twittered and cooed. (*Twittering and cooing sounds.*) Miss Cerise Chapeau, a dainty young maiden, came strolling in. (*To music of Rig-a-jig, a fat young woman bounces in from the left.*) She was feeling sad for her sweetheart had just left her for good. (*Music is "Good-bye, My Lover, Good-bye.*) He preferred horses to women; they were more profitable. (*Music is "Camptown Races."*) Cerise was weary. She sat down to rest. (CERISE *sits on the floor and music becomes "Ah! I Have Sighed to Rest Me."*) Then she heard a strange sound off in the distance. (*Loud wolf whistles. Music is "See, the Conquering Hero Comes."*) Cerise listened attentively, then in from the right walked Wolfgang Wolfson, the handsome hero, a charming chap. (WOLF, *looking like a tramp, enters to the music of "For He's a Jolly Good Fellow."*) Wolf asked Cerise to come for a stroll, first handing her a rose. (*Music is "Last Rose of Summer" and* WOLF *hands* CERISE *a crushed paper rose.*) She shakes her head in refusal. He pleads. (*Music becomes "Oh, Come, Come Away."*) After a quiet tender conversation she consented, though her mother had always told her to beware of strange men. (*Music is "Sweet and Low" and* WOLF *becomes angry and appears to threaten her.*) At last she began to feel that she had met her own true love. (*Music is "There's a Meeting Here Tonight."*) She remembered her dear old grandmother at home (*Music is "Home, Sweet Home"*) but she knew she could not leave Wolf. (*Music is "How Can I Leave Thee."*) He was truly her ideal. (*Music becomes "For He's a Jolly Good Fellow."*) She followed him trustingly into the woods. (*They go off-stage at left, arm in arm.*) Suddenly a faint cry broke the silence of the night. (*Loud shrieks off stage at the left.*) What could it be? (*Music is "What Can the Matter Be?"*) Then all was still. (*Music is "Sleep, Baby, Sleep."*) Wolf, looking sad, returns alone. (WOLF *enters at Left, grinning wickedly and rubbing hands in glee. Music is "How Can I Leave Thee?"*)

And Cerise Chapeau was never seen again. Neither was the Wolf. This was indeed a strange, sad story that happened long ago. (*Music is "Long, Long Ago."*)

SURE CURE or YOUR MANIA BACK
A PANTOMIME

The scene is the office of a psychiatrist. On the wall are signs reading: SURE CURE, PROFESSOR CALMYOUDOWN, PRACTICING PSYSCHIATRIST, LEAVE YOUR TROUBLES HERE, etc. The only furniture is a couch, a chair, and a small table on which is a large box. On the couch, resting, is the psychiatrist. He jumps up as a patient rushes in, hair on end, clothes disarranged. Patient lies on the couch. When asked his trouble he starts telling what seems to be a very wild story; he jumps up, rushes about, gesticulating wildly, apparently telling of a fist fight and a shooting, showing all possible emotions greatly exaggerated. The psychiatrist is alarmed and tries in vain to calm him. At last the psychiatrist takes a huge pill from the box on the table and tries to persuade the patient to swallow it, but the ravings grow worse. The psychiatrist, in despair, takes the pill himself and at once sinks, unconscious, to the couch. The patient looks at him in angry astonishment, reads the signs to himself, shakes his head in disgust and rushes out.

CHARADES ABOUT
FAMOUS PEOPLE

After the name is acted the players have one guess, being called upon in regular order, each member of the group having a number. The one answering wrongly is out of the game. Here are some names with which to start the game:

JACK-THE-RIPPER. Boy tears pages from a book. Offstage voice calls: "Jack, stop that!"

QUEEN ISABELLA. Woman with a toy telephone is talking earnestly. "Hello, Chris. So you haven't been scalped yet! Name the country after me, of course. Don't let the sailors throw you overboard on the way home! Good-bye, Chris."

DIOGENES. A man in a long cape and a wide-brimmed hat enters. He carries a huge flashlight which he turns on the members of the audience, looking at them searchingly. He shakes his head despairingly as if not finding what he is looking for, an honest man.

BENJAMIN FRANKLIN. A boy in shabby clothing stands eating a large bun. A pretty girl passes by and looks at him with interest.

QUEEN VICTORIA. A woman, stuffed with pillows, marshmallows in her cheeks so she looks fat, watches some boys who turn somersaults, and do stunts, clown fashion. She shakes head and looks bored, not even smiling. She mutters, "Not amused."

JULIET. Girl enters, eating a large sandwich. Voice offstage calls "Julie, come eat." Girl answers, "I did. I et."

KING TUT. Boy with a gilt paper crown on his head

enters, looks around, shakes his head in disgust and says, "Tut, tut!"

BABE RUTH. Girl enters with a doll. Another girl comes in, looks at the doll and says, "Cute! What's her name?" First girl answers, "Ruth." Second girl says, "Some babe."

MARY PICKFORD. A woman is looking at pictures of cars. A friend enters and says, "Mary, selecting a new car?" Mary answers, "Yes, and I can't decide between a Buick or a Cadillac." Friend says, "Well, I like a Ford myself. Better choose a Ford, Mary."

CARRIE NATION. Girl carrying a magazine meets another girl who says, "What's that you're reading?" First girl answers, "The Nation. It's a swell magazine. I'm taking it to my sister. I always carry the things I've read over to her."

PANTOMIMED CHARADES

The director announces each charade by telling whether it is a word or a sentence. If a word, he tells the number of syllables; if a sentence, the number of words.

WORDS THAT MIGHT BE USED:

Connection. Actor studies from a book—*con.* Touches the neck several times—*neck.* Another person comes on stage. The first person refuses to look at him and turns away—*shun.* To show the whole word, join the pieces of paper together in a line with paper clips. *Connection.*

Innocent. Drops papers in a box—*in.* Shakes head violently—*no.* Takes a penny from a purse, looks at it, puts it back—*cent.* To show the whole word, another person enters and in sweeping gestures accuses the first person of taking her pocketbook. The first person insists, clutching her pocketbook and waving her hands wildly, that she is not guilty. *Innocent.*

Other words may be: mutilate—mew-tie-late; fanciful—fan-sigh-full; matador—mat-a-door; tiptoe—tip-toe; handicap—hand-eye-cap; candidate—can-die-date; hydraulic—high-draw-lick; triplicate—trip-lick-ate.

FOR SENTENCES TRY THESE:

Better late than never. Man enters, looks at his watch, shakes his head, walks about impatiently, then angrily, looking at the watch frequently. A girl enters just as he is about to leave. She apologizes in pantomime; he smiles and takes her arm, and they leave.

OTHER SENTENCES MAY BE:

A rolling stone gathers no moss. He who hesitates is lost. Where there's smoke there's fire. It's never too late to mend. Don't waste your breath. Catch as catch can. A pain in the neck. Don't bite the hand that feeds you.

OUT OF THE NIGHT
(A humorous pantomime reading with sound effects)

FOR FOUR MEN, THREE WOMEN, NARRATOR AND EXTRAS

CHARACTERS

STAGE MANAGER
NARRATOR

In the pantomime

SMITH, *the author*
ROSELLA MAE MONTMORENCY, *the beautiful heroine*
MICHAEL PATRICK MCDOONE, *her lover*
MR. MONTMORENCY, *her father*
MRS. MONTMORENCY, *her mother*
STRANGER, *the villain*
BOSTON BETSEY, *his accomplice*
ANY NUMBER OF DANCERS

COSTUMES AND CHARACTERISTICS.—Smith wears a light business suit; Rosella Mae, a pretty flowered dress. She looks beautiful but dumb. Michael wears a weird mixture of clothing: riding boots, overalls, sweater, etc., and is heavily adorned with medals. Or, if desired, he may wear ordinary summer attire, with many medals on his coat. Mr. and Mrs. Montmorency wear fur coats, hoods, boots, etc., and are covered with artificial snow and icicles. Stranger is dressed as a tramp. Boston Betsey has a Boston accent and is very well dressed in a light tailored suit, covered with a wet raincoat, which she discards after her entrance. The dancers wear thin, bright yellow ballet dresses.

PROPERTIES.—For Smith, typewriter and paper, traveling bag. For Boston Betsey, a huge burlap bag, supposed to be a handbag containing money.

———

NOTE.—All sounds should come from offstage, made by the director and his assistants. All the movements of the pantomime characters, as well as the sounds, should be greatly exaggerated.

———

The STAGE MANAGER *comes before the curtain and addresses the audience.*

———

STAGE MANAGER. Ladies and gentlemen, your attention, please. We are going to present a play in which the actors say nothing, which in itself should be a very pleasing idea, but in which they merely act. In other words, we are giving you a pantomime. This particular pantomime, called "Out of the Night," is the story of a lonely house in the country. Sounds commonplace, doesn't it? But the story is produced by a man who, for years, has been in charge of sound effects in a major radio studio. Please don't blame me for anything that happens. I'm only the stage manager. I have to do as I'm told. (*From off stage comes a shrill "Hst!"*) Pardon me, please. That's the producer now. I'll just see what he wants. (*Goes off at right, returning at once.*) He thought I was talking too much. He doesn't care for conversation. You will now see "Out of the Night," a pantomime enacted by noted Thespians in the class of ———. (*Current year.*) The narrator is ———. (*Goes off at right.*)

———

SCENE: *To the soft music of "Home, Sweet Home," the curtain rises, showing a plain but comfortable living room. At center back, is a large open window,* '*through which is seen a garden gay with flowers. Two doors at right and left respectively are hidden by tall, old-fashioned screens. Up extreme left is a small table on which* SMITH *places his typewriter. Beside it stands a straight-backed chair. If this arrangement is too difficult, a dark cyclorama may be used as a backdrop, and baskets and vases of flowers may be grouped near it.*

The NARRATOR *enters at right and takes his position down extreme right, where he remains throughout the action.*

NARRATOR.
Thackeray Walter Scott Thomas Hardy Rex Stout Smith was a very successful author. How could he help it, with a name like that? But he was very tired this June in the year ————. (*Current year.*) Even authors, like readers, grow weary sometimes. Smith had promised the "Atlantic Weekly" a story, and it was due in just two days. He needed a calm, serene atmosphere in which to think, away from the noise and interruptions of the crowded city. He remembered the little vine-clad cottage at the foot of the mountain. "There," he said to himself, "I can work undisturbed. In one night I can plot a story really worthy of my talent—a delicate, ethereal legend of the finer, nobler things in life." So he packed up his typewriter, paper, an eraser, and a box of crackers, in case he was too busy to cook, and started for Willow Walk. It was just sunset when he stole quietly into the cottage.

(*There is a loud crash off left.* SMITH *stumbles in, puts the typewriter on table, other baggage on the floor under the table, opens the machine, inserts the paper, and sits in the pose of Rodin's "Thinker."*)

The last rays of the setting sun danced in through the west windows like golden sprites.

The DANCERS *enter at right to the music of "Blue Danube Waltz" by Strauss, or any other well-known dance music. As they do a gay dance, the light grows gradually fainter. When they dance offstage, the room is in dusk.*

As the sun dropped behind the hills (*dull thud offstage*), leaving the room in a soft dusk, Smith had an inspiration. His heart beat a triumphant accompaniment as he began to type rapidly. (*A drum beats softly offstage in march time as he types.*) His spirits bubbled with joy. At last he had a plot. This is how it began.

On a starlit June evening, the heroine, Rosella Mae Montmorency, drove up in her Rolls-Royce runabout to the deserted cottage at Willow Walk. (*Loud noises of chugging and backfiring.*) Here she was to meet her lover, Michael Patrick McDoone, just returned from a long and dangerous secret mission. She was meeting him here because her snobbish parents objected to his humble origin. As she tripped into the room (ROSELLA *enters at left and trips on the mat by the door*), she was very happy. Her heart sang. (*Soprano voice off stage sings a stanza of any popular love song.*) As she sat by the window and waited (*she sits*), she listened to the sighing of the summer breezes (*off-stage sighs as if from a mighty bellows*) and the murmuring of the tiny insects in the garden. (*Assorted sounds of bees, flies, frogs, tree toads, etc.*)

The moon rose, flooding the room with golden light. (*Very abruptly room is filled with very bright light, and a sound as of rushing water is heard*). Still Michael Patrick McDoone delayed his coming.

Just then she heard some one at the door. (*From off right come three knocks and a ring.*) She listened, puzzled. "What can it be?" she asks herself. "I'll listen again." (*Knocks and rings are repeated.*) "It can't be opportunity," murmured Rosella Mae, "because opportunity knocks only once. It can't be the postman because the postman always rings twice. So it must be Mike."

In marched a vicious-looking stranger. (STRANGER *enters at left in step to the music of any familiar march played with heavily accented rhythm.*) Rosella Mae shrieked loudly in terror (*faint squeak*), but the stranger advanced determinedly.

"Have you brought it?" he asked.

"Brought what?" the frightened girl faltered.

"The money—the ten thousand dollars. The job is done, and I want my pay. McDoone won't interfere with our Crime League any more."

Rosella Mae's teeth chattered with terror. (*Loud clicking noise.*) For whom had the wretch mistaken her? Then his words rang a bell in her mind. (*Bell clangs loudly offstage.*) He thought she was a member of the notorious Crime League. She must stall him off until the hero came. But how? She dropped her eyes. (*Dull thud.*) Wild thoughts raced through her brain. (*The sound of a racing motor is heard.*)

"You're Mattie Harry, ain't you?" the man barked. (*Barks.*)

"Of course," she answered. "Sit down and rest. I'll get the money in a minute."

As he slumped wearily into a chair (*sound as of heavy bag sliding down from a high pile*), there was no sound but the ticking of a clock in another room (*loud ticks*) and the murmur of the insects in the garden. (*Assorted insects sounds as before.*) The moonlight grew pale and faint. (*Stage light softens gradually.*)

Then the silence was broken by a low whistle. (*Loud siren blows offstage, followed by a loud splintering sound.*)

"It's them! Give me the money; they're waitin' for me. I've gotta go!" the stranger said, jumping up. (*Jumps high in the air as he rises.*)

Just at that moment, Rosella Mae saw the door handle turn. The door swung open noiselessly. (*Sound of creaking hinges at right.*) And in crept a woman. (BETSEY *crawls on at right on her hands and knees.*) She pulled herself erect when she saw the stranger. (*Sound of a pulley.*)

"You!" she hissed. (*Loud hisses offstage.*) "I swam the river to get here first. You shall not have the money. I erased McDoone, not you."

The stranger turned green with jealous rage. (*Green spotlight is turned on his face.*) "I thought you was back in Barnegat, Boston Betsey," he cried, "so I come for the dough."

"Who is this woman?" snapped Boston Betsey, glaring at Rosella Mae. (*Loud snapping sounds offstage.*) "Why—Mattie Harry, ain't she?" growled the stranger. (*Growls from offstage.*)

"No! She is an impostor—a spy! Mata Hari is in the hospital with the measles. But she hid the money in this cottage. I must find it," said Boston Betsey. "You guard this woman while I search the place."

Boston Betsey left the room. The Stranger gave Rosella Mae a searching glance (*spotlight is turned in her face for a moment*), but she was conscious of nothing save the fluttering of her frightened heart. (*Fluttering noises as of huge wings.*)

Once again all was silence, save for the distant sounds made by Boston Betsey as she searched for the money

(*loud bangings and slammings*), the ticking of the clock
(*ticks*), the soft sighing of the summer breeze (*loud
sighs*), and the murmur of the insects in the garden.
(*Assorted insect noises.*)   Occasionally a termite could
be heard, chewing the solid mahogany wainscoting,
daintily but hungrily.   (*Loud gnawing sound, made by
the sandpaper offstage.*)   It was a perfect, peaceful
night.

And then—footsteps outside in the garden.   Faint
footsteps.   (*Heavy tramping as if on stone walks.*)
The sound of an argument.   (*Machine gun fire.*)   Boston Betsey ran back into the room, the money in a
handbag, and motioned to the stranger to follow her.

"We'll take the dame, so she can't talk," he said.

"That's what you think, my friend.   Unhand the
lady!" roared a voice from the door.   (*Lion-like roars.*)

"Michael!" sang out Rosella Mae.   (*Soprano voice
sings the scales.*)

"The F.B.I.!" groaned Boston Betsey and the
stranger as they stumbled out into the night, where
justice waited for them.   (*Loud groans.*)

"My Rosella Mae!" said Michael, tossing his gun
lightly aside (*throws it down with a loud crash*), as she
fell into his arms.   (*She literally falls.   He catches her
just in time.*)

Mr. and Mrs. Montmorency enter the cottage just as
this happy reunion took place.   "My daughter!" each
said in icy tones.   (*Sound of splintering ice offstage.*)

Mr. Smith—you haven't forgotten him, have you?
He's the author—was startled by the appearance of Mr.
and Mrs. Montmorency, in every sense of the word.

"I thought it was June," he muttered to himself.
"Oh, well, time flies fast when you're working hard, as I
always say."

"Mother, father," gasped Rosella Mae (*loud gasps*),

"you can no longer refuse your consent to our marriage. Michael Patrick McDoone is a member of the F.B.I., of the Northwestern Mounted Police, and of Donovan's Detective Agency. Besides which, he is a hero. He just killed all the Crime League gang—I hope. Didn't you, Michael?"

"And how!" laughed Michael, picking up his gun. (*Loud laughter.*)

Mr. and Mrs. Montmorency, after long and serious reflection, (*they look at each other once—and nod assent immediately*) gave their consent, and one could almost hear wedding bells on the breeze. (*Clang of firebells, changing abruptly to chimes.*)

The four left happily. (MICHAEL *and* ROSELLA MAE *walk back of* ROSELLA's *parents and* MICHAEL's *gun, unconsciously, is pointed at* MR. MONTMORENCY's *back.*)

The little cottage was once more deserted. All was quiet save the ticking of the clock (*ticks*), the sighing of the summer breeze (*loud sighs*), the murmur of the insects in the garden (*assorted insect noises*), and occasionally the faint sound of termites gnawing the solid mahogany wainscoting, daintily but hungrily. (*Gnawing, crushing sound.*) It was a still, peaceful night in the country. Mr. Smith's story was finished. He gathered up his papers, closed his typewriter, stretched himself (*creaking noise as he stretches*), and started home, happy in the consciousness of a task well done, even though he was still a trifle confused about the plot. He had quite forgotten the box of crackers, doubtless the termites ate them before morning. He went silently out into the night. (*Loud crash as he goes off at left.*) All was quiet, save the tick of the clock (*ticks*), the soft sighing of the summer breeze (*loud sighing*), the murmur of the insects in the garden. (*Assorted insect noises.*)

(The curtain falls during the assorted noises.)

STAGE MANAGER *(coming before the curtain).* You remember I told you the producer had been a sound effects man. That accounts for anything you didn't understand about Mr. Smith's story or the pantomime. *(Noises of a fight offstage. A loud voice says, "You ruined it!")* That's the author. I guess he didn't like it, either. Well, good night, friends. Better luck next time. *(Exit.)*

———

LOCHINVAR LEADBETTER
(*A shadow play*)

FOR FOUR MEN, EIGHT WOMEN, AND EXTRAS

CHARACTERS

NARRATOR

In the shadow play

LOCHINVAR, *a hero*
COUNTRY LASS
CRONE
ATHLETIC GIRL
SOPHISTICATED GIRL ⎬ *applicants for acting jobs*
BUSINESS WOMAN
TRAGEDY QUEEN
VILLAINESS

DORINDA DALE, *Lochinvar's beloved*
ATHLETIC INSTRUCTOR
MINISTER
ANY NUMBER OF WEDDING GUESTS
SIX SMALL CHILDREN

PRODUCTION NOTES

Shadow plays are great fun, being easy to do and having no lines, no scenery, costumes, or make-up. But they should be rehearsed several times. A curtain of white, unbleached muslin or very heavy cheesecloth should be used and stretched very taut. It would be well to go over it with a soaking wet sponge just before the play begins. The moisture removes all wrinkles from the cloth and aids in producing a sharp, clear shadow. About two feet behind the curtain on the floor, a strong light with a reflector is placed, and all lights in the

room are extinguished. Whatever scenery is desired
may be cut from cardboard and pinned to the curtain.
Actors should play with profiles to the audience, to keep
gestures of arms and hands clear. All action should
be exaggerated. The nearer he stands to the curtain,
the larger the actor appears. When he disappears, he
jumps over the light. The style of costumes should be
exaggerated; e.g., a picture hat should be enormous,
and a high hat very high. Music is important and
should fit the mood of the action.

The narrator stands at the side of the screen or curtain out of sight of the audience, as in a puppet show.
As he reads the narrative, he should pause wherever
action occurs or music is indicated, until the actors have
finished their pantomime or the music ceases.

NARRATOR.

Friends, in this prosaic world we are prone to forget
the finer things of life. In the struggle for riches—
after all, why struggle?—it doesn't do any good. We
overlook romance. Think of the great love stories of
the world: Romeo and Juliet, Tristan and Isolde, Ab-
bott and Costello, the Prince and Cinderella, Mickey
Mouse and Minnie, Launcelot and—er—er— Think of
the great love stories of the world. We are about to
show you one: the inspiring story of Lochinvar Leadbetter (1).

Lochinvar Leadbetter was a lonely lad. He com-
muned with nature (A). His college chums, with whom
he never felt at ease because their minds were worlds
apart from his, spent their leisure hours celebrating
athletic victories (2) (B). Lochinvar loved classic
literature. He could recite yards of it, from Hamlet's
soliloquy to "Thanatopsis"; from "Paradise Lost" to

"The Deserted Village." And that, my friends, is some trip (3) (C).

Some people thought Lochinvar was a sissy, but were they mistaken, as we shall show you. When Lochinvar left college, he hesitated in choosing a profession. His father wanted him to be a plumber, his mother wanted him to be a poet, but Lochinvar wanted to be a hero (4). So he became a theatrical agent. He opened an office down town (D), and there he interviewed beautiful girls and some not so beautiful (5), all looking for jobs. They came, day after day, displaying their—er—acting ability. Young girls from the country (E); wicked old crones, ripe for villainy (F); athletic dames who prized brawn more than beauty (G); sophisticated females, the station-wagon and country club type (H); business women who wanted only a career (I); the tragic twerp, who thought herself a second Sarah Siddons (J); the villainess, with fatal fascination (K). But they each left Lochinvar unmoved. He usually got them jobs, in time, but he never remembered which was who or who was what till he looked them up in the files (L).

Then, one day, something happened that changed Lochinvar's whole life. He saw Dorinda Dale, the girl of his dreams (6). She entered his office, looking for a job as ingénue in a road company of "East Lynne" (M). She was a nice girl, not too bright; but then so few of us are! She was young, she was pretty, she loved nature, she loved poetry, and Lochinvar loved her from the moment he saw her. He got her the job. He went home that night reeling with happiness (7) (N).

But the next day Dorinda came back, and with her a man, Gareth Gale. That was his stage name. His real name was Chuck Jones. Dorinda introduced him as her fiancé. Poor Lochinvar nearly fainted (8). (O) Chuck said Dorinda could not take the job, as they were to be married the next evening and go to live in Scotland, where he was a professional golfer (9).   Dorinda, being a sweet little thing, apologized for breaking her contract and invited Lochinvar to the wedding.

When they left, Lochinvar was broken-hearted, but he was brave. He pulled himself together (P). He tried to think of some way to prevent this terrible marriage and get Dorinda for himself. It was of no use (10). Then he sat down and read to quiet his throbbing nerves.   He read that famous old ballad of Walter Scott, "Lochinvar," the bold hero for whom he had been named. Now he knew what to do. He would live up to his name (11). Out he went into the night, determination in his heart and all his money in his pocket.

All through the night he toiled (12). He learned to box. He learned to shoot. He learned to fence. He exhausted his instructors but he remained fresh and cool as one of the daisies he loved (Q).

As morning light began to fill the gym, he realized in horror that the most difficult task still lay before him. He had to learn to ride a horse. He had a motorcycle, but that was not romantic. Imagine Lochinvar on a motorcycle! No, I can't either! He went sadly out of the gym to the riding stable near by (13). We shall spare you the sight of Lochinvar learning to ride a wild steed. You would find it as painful as did he. But we shall show you Lochinvar coming home at noon. He had learned to ride (R).

He slept and dreamed of daisy-filled meadows, of soft summer moonlight and, of course, of Dorinda (14).

The hours danced by (15). It was eight o'clock. Wedding bells were pealing. At the home of Dorinda, the bridal party entered the living room to the strains of sweet music (16). Just as the ceremony was about to begin (S), the sound of galloping hoofs was heard outside. All turned in surprise. Then the guests started back in horror, as a strange man rushed into the room, socked Chuck on the jaw with ease and pleasure, knocking him out, seized the bride in his arms, and disappeared, all before you could say, "Abduction." The guests fainted with horror, but the organist merely changed her tune (17).

"My hero," sighed Dorinda, as Lochinvar carried her out into the moonlight and she saw who he was.

"Come. My fleet steed is waiting," he replied (1) (T).

So Lochinvar lifted Dorinda to the saddle, mounted himself—on the wrong side, but after all he'd had only four hours' practice—and away they went (13) (U). "They'll have fleet steeds that follow," he quoted, as they galloped over hill and dale, mountain and valley, and anything else that got in their way.

As they rode away into the misty moonlight, Dorinda was happy. She'd never liked Chuck, anyway. Lochinvar was happy because he had won the fair Dorinda, and because he had proved what he had long suspected. He was a hero. He had lived up to the name of Lochinvar (4).

In the long years that followed, Dorinda and Lochinvar were very happy, and the horse remained one of the most cherished members of the Leadbetter family. But Lochinvar never rode again. He still recites poetry, and often in the summer evenings he and his little family say poems in concert—excerpts from the great literature of the ages. Their favorite selection is "Lochinvar," by Walter Scott (11) (V).

PANTOMIME

A. Lochinvar picks a daisy, smells it, puts in button hole.
B. College boys march past waving banners as Lochinvar leaves.

C. Lochinvar returns, books under arm, reading as he walks, and stubs his toe.
D. Lochinvar sits at desk in office. He shakes head in displeasure—at all girls but Dorinda.
E. Country girl enters, acts coy, recites, with gestures and no pep, a nursery rime, and leaves.
F. Old crone enters, does same rime in a blood-curdling way, and leaves.
G. Athletic girl enters, makes a gymnastic exercise of the rime, and leaves.
H. Sophisticated female enters, acts bored, smokes as she recites, and leaves.
I. Business woman strides in, times herself by her wrist watch, rattles off a short speech in pantomime, and leaves.
J. Tragic woman enters. She wears a long veil and is very dramatic; leaves with sweeping gesture of disgust at her failure.
K. Sinister girl draws a gun when she recites, then leaves.
L. Lochinvar searches files.
M. Dorinda enters the office, acts natural, gets the job, then leaves.
N. Lochinvar reels out.
O. Dorinda returns to the office with Chuck, who swaggers and shakes hands so firmly he nearly cripples Lochinvar. He shakes his fist threateningly at Lochinvar till he returns the money to Dorinda. Chuck and Dorinda leave.
P. Lochinvar literally pulls himself together, takes an aspirin from bottle produced from his pocket and sits down to read from book on desk. He throws the book down, takes money from the desk, puts it in his pocket, and runs off stage.
Q. Lochinvar is in the gym, an empty room, boxing with his instructor. He shoots at a target set up by instructor, and then he learns to fence. Instructor, exhausted, faints. Lochinvar rushes out.
R. Lochinvar comes home at noon. A bright sun is in the sky. Lochinvar is so lame he can scarcely walk.
S. Flowers are banked in a room. The minister is waiting. The bridal party enters. The minister raises his hand. All turn as hoofbeats are heard. (Cocoanut shells offstage.) They start in horror. Lochinvar rushes in, hits Chuck in the jaw, knocking him out, grabs Dorinda and rushes out. The guests all faint, including the minister.
T. Dorinda and Lochinvar are talking. He urges her not to delay.
U. A rocking-horse is at center, Dorinda mounted behind Lochinvar. To give the effect of movement have bushes and trees cut from cardboard and mounted on rollers, a long string of scenery attached to a rope. Someone at right starts it rolling and someone at left pulls it across the stage rapidly. This gives the idea of rapid motion. To conceal

rollers and ropes from the audience, at the base of the screen is a thick row of shrubbery, which may be there all the time, even during the office scene. There is a moon in the sky.

V. The Leadbetter family—Lochinvar, Dorinda, and six children of assorted sizes—are reciting in pantomime the poem, "Lochinvar," with dramatic gestures.

INCIDENTAL MUSIC

1. Flower Song (Lange)
2. Boola Song
3. Pilgrims' Chorus from "Tannhäuser"
4. Hail to the Chief
5. Dancing Doll (Poldini)
6. Sleeping Beauty Waltz (Tchaikovsky)
7. Any Virginia reel
8. Golliwog's Cakewalk (Debussy)
9. Bluebells of Scotland
10. The Heart Bowed Down (Balfe)
11. Loch Lomond
12. For He's a Jolly Good Fellow
13. De Camptown Races
14. Traumerei (Schumann)
15. Dance of the Hours from "La Gioconda"
16. Bridal Chorus from "Lohengrin"
17. Funeral March (Chopin)

If a piano is used, the few measures needed from each selection should be copied on one music folio so that the pianist may avoid the frantic turning of pages and searching for music. If records are used, one person should be assigned the task of changing them. In places where there is not time even for a quick change, it would be well to have an extra phonograph to play the few measures needed.

LONG, LONG AGO
(*A reading with sound effects*)

This stunt calls for a narrator and a number of people to produce the sounds, which must be made at exactly the right moment. The narrator should pause briefly while the sound is made, so that it will not drown out his next words. If someone sufficiently skillful is available, he may handle all the properties and produce all the sounds at the side of the stage, where the audience can see him. If preferred, this stunt may be given as a pantomime, with the cast of four characters making all the appropriate motions on the stage. But the sound effects should still be used, either on or off the stage.

Just before the story begins, the music of "Long, Long Ago" is played, and the narrator comes before the audience.

NARRATOR. I am going to tell you a sad little story of the long ago. Get out your handkerchiefs. You'll need 'em, for this is a tale well calculated to keep you in tears—and terror.

Many, many years ago Rosalie Rickenback lived in a little cottage on the banks of the Rushtothesea River in the county of Willewawaw. She lived alone except for her faithful maid servant, Viola. But Rosalie was not lonely, for she had a sweetheart, Burton Blaine, and they were to be married soon.

Across the meadows, at the foot of the hill, lived Irwin Dean—a louse if ever there was one. He, too, loved Rosalie. She repulsed all his advances; and Irwin was some advancer!

The invitations were out to Rosalie's wedding. Even the cakes were ready. Then one night a terrible storm came up. It wasn't a fit night for man or beast to be out in—not even Irwin. That night something happened.

The next morning some friends dropped in. When they reached the cottage they were met by perfect silence. Entering, they found Rosalie, Viola, Burton, and Irwin, lying on the floor dead. To this day nobody knows what happened—that is, nobody but me. That is the story I am going to tell you. I can see clearly, in my imagination, the events of that terrible night so long ago. It all happened like this:

Rosalie busied herself about the room, arranging flowers and fluffing up the pillows, preparing for the arrival of Burton. She choked back her amusement (1), as she thought how angry Irwin would be when he returned from the city the next week and found her married and gone. As her glance swept the room (2) a strange thought shot through her mind (3). What if Irwin were to return before the wedding? Her spirits fell (4). She heard Viola clattering in the kitchen, (5) and she felt better.

A storm approached. Far off in the distance, as night fell (4), she heard the whir of a plane (6). The wind whistled (7). The trees groaned (8). Rosalie was worried about Burton. Just then Viola danced into the room (9), happy as usual. Viola rubbed her hands in glee (10) and told her mistress the clams were all opened and the biscuits baked for supper, which would be ready whenever Burton arrived. Viola rolled her eyes in pride (11) as she spoke of the biscuit. Then, puffing like a locomotive (12), back to the kitchen she went.

Rosalie was tired; her head was spinning (13). Outside the wind sobbed (14). The trees groaned (8). The river roared (15). It was a wild night. Suddenly above the groaning of the trees (8), the roaring of the river (15), and the sobbing of the wind (14), she heard the sound of horse's hoofs (16). Burton was coming. Her heart sang for joy (17). In marched Burton (18). He always marched; he had the habit. He had been a corporal in the last war. Rosalie coyly dropped her eyes, as she greeted him (4). The trees groaned (8). The wind sobbed (14), and the river roared (15). It was a wild night. But Rosalie and Burton were happy. Something in the storm struck a chord (19) in their hearts, and Rosalie wiped away her tears (20).

Again she heard the plane (6). The sound rang a bell in her mind (21). Could it be Irwin? She told Burton of her fears, and the words acted like a trumpet call to his bravery (22).

"Fear not," he said. "I will protect you."

Just then, in rushed Irwin, gritting his teeth (23) in rage. Rosalie and Burton stood as if nailed to the spot (24). Rosalie's heart beat like a trip hammer (25). Viola, entering from the kitchen, saw Irwin, staggered to a corner, and collapsed (26).

Rosalie ran to Burton's arms. She was shaking like a leaf (27). Burton's mouth shut like a trap (28). He put his hand in his pocket, but Irwin shook his head (27). He could not be bribed, and besides he had more money than Burton (29).

"Beat it," growled Burton (30).

Rosalie tore herself away from Burton (31). She swallowed her tears (32).

"Come with me to the casbah," snarled Irwin (33), "or I will kill both you and your lover."

She knew Irwin had a gun and Burton had a gun. Funny how those boys always carried guns!

In the corner Viola batted her eyelashes (34). Outside the trees groaned (8), the wind sobbed (14), and the river roared (15). It was a wild night. Rosalie slithered to the floor in a faint (35). As she did so, both men fired their guns at once (36). And at once both men dropped dead (4). Viola went to Rosalie's side and tried to comfort her. Their tears fell like rain (37). The horror of it all! Invitations out, and no wedding—and all that food wasted! Broken-hearted, Rosalie and Viola fell to the floor, dead (4).

Outside, the riderless horse galloped away (16). A plane whirred by (6), the river roared (15), the wind sobbed (14), and the trees groaned (8). It was a wild night. (*A few measures of the storm music from "William Tell" are played by the pianist.*)

And that, my friends, is the true story of what happened in that little cottage, on that fateful night long, long ago.

(*The pianist plays the last four measures of the music of "Long, Long Ago."*)

SOUND EFFECTS

1. Sound of choking. Be realistic.
2. Pass a large broom over a rough surface to make the sound of sweeping.
3. Sound of a single shot.
4. Let something fairly heavy drop to the floor.
5. Bang pots and pans together and crackle cellophane.
6. Turn on a huge electric fan.
7. Blow blast on a large whistle.
8. Groan loudly.
9. Sound of tap dancing.
10. Rub together two pieces of sandpaper.
11. Roll marbles over a piece of tin.

12. Imitate a locomotive.
13. Imitate the whirring sound of a turning wheel or top.
14. Sob loudly.
15. Roar like a lion.
16. Use cocoanut shells on hard wood to make sound of hoofs.
17. A high soprano voice sings trills.
18. To music of any march (a few bars) stamp in time heavily.
19. Strike a loud chord on the piano.
20. Swishing sound.
21. Ring a dinner bell.
22. Play a measure on a trumpet. Use record if no trumpeters are available.
23. Stir a pile of small stones violently.
24. Hammer nails into a board.
25. With a large hammer strike blows in rhythm on a hard surface.
26. Puncture a large balloon.
27. Shake pebbles in a tin can. Shake louder for Irwin's head.
28. Slap two pieces of metal together.
29. Rattle pieces of metal together.
30. Growl like a cross dog.
31. Tear a piece of heavy cloth.
32. Gulping sound.
33. Snarl fiercely like a tiger.
34. Hit a board several times with a baseball bat.
35. Drag a heavy article over the floor to make a slithering sound.
36. Fire two blank cartridges, one a second after the other.
37. Pour water from a sprinkler into a tin pan.

ONE SUMMER NIGHT
(*A burlesque pantomime reading with music*)

This stunt requires only a narrator and a pianist. All the sounds are imitated on the piano. Before the story begins, the pianist plays something soothing, like Lange's "Flower Song" or Schubert's "Moment Musical." Then the narrator comes forward and addresses the assembly.

NARRATOR (*speaking very dramatically*). Friends, I am going to tell you a story which illustrates perfectly the triumph of right over wrong, of good over evil, and of anything else you happen to think of. Listen well.

The pianist plays Schumann's "Traumerei." As the narrator tells the story and mentions the various people and things listed below, the pianist makes the sounds on the piano intended to describe or suggest them. The narrator should pause and give the pianist time to finish each sound before resuming his narrative.

NARRATOR. It was a lovely summer evening. The soft winds blew gently through the treetops (1). Lucile, our heroine (2), walked in the garden. She looked up into the deep blue sky, where shone the evening star (3). She wished her hero, Major Domo (4) were safe home from the war. In the bushes the night birds sang tender love songs (5). Lucile (2) felt sad, and her tears fell like rain (6). She missed her Major Domo (4). The soft wind blew (1), the evening star shone (3), the night birds sang (5), and Lucile (2) wept (6).

Then a shadow fell across her path. It was Desmond Donahue, the villain (7), who lived next door. He looked

desperate, and when he said softly, "At last, my proud
beauty, I have you in my power," Lucile (2) was scared
(8). She feared Desmond Donahue (7), and with good
reason.

"If Major Domo (4) were here," gasped Lucile (2),
"you would not dare address me."

"Ha, ha!" laughed Desmond Donahue (7). "I fear
no man, not even a four-star general. Certainly not a
mere Major Domo" (4).

The birds sang in the bushes (5), the wind blew
through the treetops (1), and the star shone softly
(3), but Lucile (2) was scared (8).

"I shall give you your choice," snarled Desmond
Donahue (7). "In my den I have a lion (9). Either
you promise to marry me, or I feed you to the lion (9)
tonight. He is hungry. You will be a dainty appetizer
for my lion" (9).

"Spare me, Desmond Donahue (7)," begged Lucile
(2). "If Major Domo (4) were here, he would kill
your wicked lion (9)."

"Ha, ha!" laughed Desmond Donahue (7). The wind
blew harder (1), the birds sang louder (5), the star
shone brighter (3), and the lion roared in the den (9).

Then it began to thunder (11). Lucile (2) could
always think—if you could call it that—best when it
was storming. She had an idea. Major Domo (4) had
left her his pet elephant (12) as a parting gift. He
couldn't afford an engagement ring. If Lucile (2) could
get the elephant (12) out of the trunk room where he
spent most of his time, the elephant (12) would scare
(8) away Desmond Donahue (7) and his lion (9). And
a storm always made the elephant (12) very cross,
anyway.

The elephant (12) would come if she whistled, but
Lucile (2) couldn't whistle. What was left for her but

the lion's den (9); and Lucile (2) was no Daniel. She must get the elephant (12) to come to the rescue.

"Desmond Donahue," said Lucile (2), "do something to keep my courage up. I can't face a thing like this unless you help me. Please whistle. Then I'll decide which I prefer—you or the lion (9)."

The wind blew a gale (10), the birds (5) ceased to sing, the star (3) went under a cloud, the thunder rolled (11), and Desmond Donahue (7) whistled. (*Here* NARRATOR *gives a loud shrill whistle of surprise.*) Lucile (2) crossed her fingers—her eyes were already crossed from fright (8); and then she heard the elephant (12) coming.

"What's that noise?" asked Desmond Donahue (7).

"It must be thunder," (11) said Lucile (2).

"Sounds like an elephant (12) to me," said Desmond Donahue (7), "but of course there's no elephant (12) around here."

"That's what you think," laughed Lucile (2), as the elephant (12) marched in boldly, seized Desmond Donahue (7) in his trunk, and tossed him clear across the yard into the lion's den (9).

Then everybody was happy. The lion (9) roared with joy because he loved Desmond Donahue (7). Lucile (2) was happy because she could go home in peace and dream of Major Domo (4). The elephant (12) was happy because he had saved Lucile (2) for his master, Major Domo (4).

The thunder (11) ceased. The gale (10) died down. Soft winds blew through the treetops (1). The birds sang (5), and the star (3) shone brightly as the elephant (12) and Lucile (2) went home together.

(*The* NARRATOR *bows, while the pianist plays* "*Home, Sweet Home.*")

DESCRIPTIVE SOUNDS

1. WIND—Scales run up and down gently
2. HEROINE—Tripping notes in treble
3. STAR—A clear high note
4. HERO—Martial strain
5. BIRDS—High trills
6. RAIN—Soft gentle tapping on one key; same for weeping
7. VILLAIN—Heavy bass note played three times
8. FRIGHT—Tremolo in treble
9. LION—Tremolo in deep bass
10. GALE—Scales run in bass glissando
11. THUNDER—Heavy chords in deep bass
12. ELEPHANT—Thumping chords repeated to indicate elephant walking

RING OUT THE BELLS
(*A series of pantomimes with music*)

The bellringer is a large woman in washerwoman attire, sleeves rolled up, wearing a big gingham apron. In front of the curtain at right stands a tall screen. Behind the screen, hidden from view, is a table, on which stands a washtub, with a wide clothes wringer attached to it. Under the table is a basket containing white cloths, each cut in the shape of a big bell or merely a towel. On each cloth in heavy black letters is printed the name of the bell. Near the table is another basket, now empty, which receives the cloths after they have been wrung.

The bellringer comes before the curtain and addresses the audience.

Bellringer.   Friends, did you ever stop to think how many different kinds of bells there are to ring?   No? You'll be surprised.   Stick around and find out.

Stage hands remove the screen, revealing the table and laundry paraphernalia. The bellringer takes her place beside the washtub and wrings out the first bell, holding it up high so that the audience may read the inscription on it. Then she drops it in the receiving basket. She repeats this process for every succeeding bell, making it last as long as possible when settings for new scenes are changed behind the curtain. All the tableaux take place back of the curtain. At the close of each tableau, the curtain falls, and the stage is cleared for the next scene.

Liberty Bell.—To music of "Liberty Bell March,"

the curtain rises. A tall, beautiful girl, dressed in cling-ing white robes and a gilt crown, holding a lamp or a torch in her hand, and made up to imitate as closely as possible the famous statue of Liberty Enlightening the World, is .seen at the center of the stage. She stands on a box painted white or covered with white material. To make the girl's hair white, lather with shaving cream and smooth it in place. Or, if preferred, the hair may be powdered white.

COWBELLS.—To the music of "Ride, Tenderfoot, Ride," the curtain rises. On the stage are a number of pretty girls in traditional cow-girl attire. They do a square dance to the music of "Oh, Susannah." Cow-bells are rung offstage.

FOG BELL.—To the music of "Anchors 'Aweigh," the curtain rises to show a small boy in bellboy uniform. His hand rests on a huge bell buoy made by covering an old hoop skirt with muslin painted purple. Inside this buoy is a very small boy, who makes it sway back and forth as if tossing on waves. The bell rings harshly, then from right, to the music of "Bell-Bottom Trousers," sailors in correct sailor suits parade jauntily across the stage. Under cover of this entrance, the two small boys leave the stage. The sailors may dance a hornpipe to the music of "Sailor's Hornpipe."

DUMBBELL.—The music is "March of the Toys," by Herbert. When the curtain rises, on the stage are any number boys and girls in gymnasium suits, doing a drill with dumbbells, directed by one of their number.

BLUE BELLS.—The music is "My Melancholy Baby."

On the stage are grouped a number of woeful maidens, prettily attired, weeping into huge handkerchiefs. Some young men enter. Each man walks off with his girl, who puts away her handkerchief and smiles happily. The bells peal merrily.

DINNER BELL.—The only music is the sound of the dinner bell ringing loudly offstage. Men, women, and children are moving back and forth on stage as if going somewhere but in no particular hurry, when suddenly the bell rings. All rush offstage in different directions. From offstage comes the shout, "Come and get it."

BICYCLE BELL.—The music is "A Bicycle Built for Two." Across the stage ride children on bicycles and tricycles and men and women on bicycles. Each rings his or her bell violently.

BELL TELEPHONE COMPANY.—The music is "Somewhere a Voice is Calling." On the stage are a few small tables, at each of which sits a man or a woman with a toy telephone, evidently trying to get a number. As each gives up the attempt and slams down the receiver, the bell rings loudly.

ALARM BELL.—The music is "Serenade" by Drigo. On the stage are two rows of cots, occupied by girls in pajamas. Beside each cot is a very small table, upon which is an alarm clock. The girls are peacefully sleeping when all the alarms go off. The girls jump out of bed as the curtain falls.

SCHOOL BELL.—To the music of "School Days," the curtain rises, revealing a crowd of bored and reluctant children, of assorted sizes, going to school, books under their arms. Back of the curtain, a bell clangs loudly, and they run offstage.

BELLE OF THE BALL.—The music is the "Merry Widow Waltz." At the center of the stage is a pretty girl in a ball dress. At the sides stand other girls. At either end of the stage are young men, who dance with the belle, cutting in rudely, while the wallflower girls look on sadly.

WEDDING BELLS.—To the music of Mendelssohn's "Wedding March," a wedding party enters, beautifully attired. The bells ring, the music grows louder, and the party moves slowly offstage as if the ceremony were over.

CHRISTMAS BELLS.—The music is "Jingle Bells." On the stage is Santa, in a huge cardboard sleigh, from which stick out trees and bundles. His reindeer are of cardboard also. Santa, in traditional costume, gets out of the sleigh and strokes the reindeer, as their bells ring loudly from offstage.

CURFEW BELL.—The music is "Star Dust" by Carmichael. The stage is dimly lighted. The street is filled with children. The curfew bell rings offstage and the children hesitate. As the bell rings again more loudly, the children shrug their shoulders and saunter off as a policeman enters from left, swinging his night stick.

FIRE BELL.—The music is the familiar round, "Scotland's Burning." As the curtain rises, the bell clangs and a siren screams. Firemen rush on the stage from left. Their engine is a long, red toy wagon or several

wagons joined together and propelled by several firemen. There is a large flashlight on the front of the
wagon. When the wagon stops, the firemen turn it a
trifle to one side so the light will shine down on the audience. The wagon should make as much noise as possible. It stops in the center of the stage. The firemen, all wearing paper hats, line up and point off right.
Each man carries a scuttle, a tin dipper, etc. Some of
the firemen carry stepladders. One has a huge fishing
net. Another has a coil of hose. They rush offstage
at right, leaving the wagon at center. The chief, wearing a huge badge and carrying a raised umbrella to
keep from getting his uniform wet, takes a folding chair
from the wagon and sits, facing the front, to watch his
men work. The crackling of flames is heard. This
sound is made by crackling stiff paper offstage at right.
There are loud shouts and then a wet, blackened fire-
man staggers on at right, carrying a huge doll that he
has rescued from the flames. Other firemen emerge after
a loud crash is heard, which indicates that the building, whatever it was, has collapsed. To make the crash,
knock over boxes and rattle tins offstage, and drop
heavy weights from a height. The driver cranks the
engine of the wagon with a stove shaker, as the chief
puts his chair back in the wagon, and the firemen prepare to drive off. If desired, pipe smoke may be blown
on stage through a rubber tube. The sound of water
on the burning building may be imitated by sprinkling
water into a large empty tin tub.

After the curtain has fallen, the last bell has been
wrung out, and the empty basket is filled with clothes,
the bellringer may come before curtain and take a bow.

THE POET'S ART GALLERY
(*A series of tableaux*)

No frame is needed, as the entire stage is the picture. The backdrop is a dark cyclorama against which painted scenes on beaverboard or paper may be attached.

The Guide should have a pleasing voice and may be either a young woman in long black skirt and white frilly blouse, or a young man in dark trousers and white shirt, open at the throat. The Guide, either man or woman, wears a red band with the words "Poet's Art Gallery" on it in gilt letters, over one shoulder and under the other.

GUIDE (*coming before curtain*). Friends, welcome to our Poet's Art Gallery. Before showing you the pictures, I shall tell you which poem each illustrates. The first poem is "The Fairies," by Allingham.

THE FAIRIES
Music: Pierne's "March of the Little Fauns"
GUIDE.

> Up the airy mountain,
>   Down the rushy glen,
> We daren't go a-hunting
>   For fear of little men.
> Wee folk, good folk,
>   Trooping all together;
> Green jacket, red cap,
>   And white owl's feather.

Tableau.—The curtain is drawn to show a painted scene of purple mountains, rocky glen, and moonlit sky on the cyclorama. As many small boys as the space will hold are grouped at the sides and in marching formation down the center. They wear tight green jackets, white trousers, white shoes and stockings, and red caps, each with a long white feather.

THE CHARGE OF THE LIGHT BRIGADE
Music: Schubert's "March Militaire"

GUIDE. You are all familiar with Tennyson's famous "Charge of the Light Brigade."

Tableau.—The curtain is drawn to show a man standing in the center of the stage, holding up so the audience may see, and wearing a shocked and enraged look, a huge sheet of paper. It is an electric light bill. At top in black letters large enough for the audience to read are the words, "Super Gas and Electric Company, May 1 to June 1, $196.74." Behind the man is his wife, her hands clasped in horror.

OLD MOTHER HUBBARD
Music: Bishop's "Home, Sweet Home"

GUIDE. You all know the old nursery rhyme:
Old Mother Hubbard went to the cupboard
  To get her poor dog a bone,
But when she got there the cupboard was bare,
  And so the poor dog had none.
Our artist has given it a modern version. Behold the Mother Hubbard of —— (*Mentions the current*

year.)

Tableau.—The curtain is drawn to reveal a large cupboard, which may be made of a portable wardrobe. The doors are open, the shelves are in great disorder, and the floor is covered with things that have fallen out—articles of clothing, boxes, brushes, cans, dishes, books, etc. Beside the cupboard stands Mother Hubbard, a stylishly dressed young woman, holding in one hand a huge box of dog biscuit, plainly labelled. At her feet is a large dog with a pink ribbon about his neck. A toy dog may be used.

ROMEO AND JULIET
Music: Rodgers' "My Heart Stool Still"

GUIDE. Shakespeare's great love story, "Romeo and Juliet," as interpreted by an inspired but hungry artist. Romeo owed, and Julie et.

Tableau.—The curtain is drawn to show, at the center of the stage, a small table, covered with empty dishes that have obviously held a good meal. Beside the table are a romantic-looking young couple in street attire. She sits in her place, smiling and full. He stands, with his pockets turned inside out and a few cents in his hand, looking tragically at the bill on the table before him. A waiter stands at the rear of the stage, regarding him with suspicion.

PIPPA PASSES
Music: Meyerbeer's "Coronation March"

GUIDE. You are, of course, familiar with Robert Browning's eloquent poem, "Pippa Passes." Now you shall see an artist's version.

Tableau.—The curtain is drawn to show a group composed of a father, mother, and daughter. The parents gaze admiringly at the young girl as she holds up a huge diploma, on which the word, "diploma," is plain enough for the audience to read. Below the word is a paragraph of print too small to be read, and then comes the name Pippa in enormous letters.

Section Five

Games for All Occasions

THE DOCTOR'S DOG

The players sit in a circle. They must describe the doctor's dog, using all the letters of the alphabet. The first player describes the dog with an adjective beginning with A—as active. Everyone in the circle describes the dog with an adjective beginning with A. Then they start again with words starting with B. The letter X may have to be omitted. Anyone who fails to supply an adjective promptly is out of the game.

TRY TO GET UP

Two players sit on the floor, back to back, arms tightly locked in front. Each tries to get up. The first one up wins.

BLIND MAN'S ORDERS

One player, blindfolded, carrying a cane, stands in the middle of the circle of players who dance around him until he taps his cane on the floor three times at which they immediately stand still. He points his cane and the player at whom it points takes hold of the end of it. The blind man says, "I order you to make a noise like a factory whistle." The player does so and the blind man tries to guess who it is. If he guesses correctly, the two change places. If not, the blind man continues to give orders, always asking for a certain noise, like that of a train, a cat, a bee, a hurricane, etc.

SPIN YOUR TOP

The players stand in a straight line, their feet together, their arms bent, ready to spring. At a signal from the leader each jumps up in the air and tries to make one or more complete spins before landing on his feet.

BEWARE OF CLUBS

Have the center of the room cleared. The players, not more than ten, stand in a line, holding hands. Six Indian clubs are placed at intervals around the room not near the wall. At a given signal the line marches, following the leader, around the room, in and out among the clubs. Anyone touching or knocking over a club is put out of line. The winner is the one who keeps clear of the clubs for a given length of time.

HANDS OFF

One player has a large inflated balloon on a string. The others surround him and try to burst the balloon as they keep going around in a circle. They may use a pin, scissors, anything, but they must keep in the circle and use but one hand. Of course the player with the balloon keeps moving around close to the circle so the would-be deflators have a sporting chance.

PICK UP YOUR FEET

The players form in a line, hands on hips, arms akimbo. They follow the leader who shouts directions, doing the action himself as he names it. They may march around the room several times. Then they are ordered by the leader to follow him in these movements: 1. Four march steps; 2. Four skips; 3. Four hops to the left; 4. Four hops to the right; 5. Four hops on the right foot; 6. Leader shouts, LOOK OUT FOR THE STEPS, takes three steps, trips and nearly falls; 7. Four march steps; 8. Four hops forward on both feet; 9. Four trotting steps; 10. Pick up your left foot; 11. Four march steps; 12. Pick up your right foot; 13. Four march steps backward; 14. Four march steps forward; 15. Two steps to right; 16. Two steps to left; 17. Pick up both feet and hold them for count of 10. As they can't do this they are dismissed in disgrace. These directions are merely suggestions. The leader may think of many interesting and difficult things to do.

WHICH NOSE BEST?

The contestants are on their knees in a straight line. In front of each contestant is a small rubber ball. At the far end of the room is a white line or tape. The players must, using the nose only, push the ball the length of the room and over the white line. The first one to get the ball over wins.

IT'S IN THE CARDS

Any number may play this game. One called the judge gives each player a card taken from a bridge pack. Only two jacks may be given out. It is explained before starting the game that the one who gets the king of clubs must kill someone. No player knows what cards the others have. The judge may either switch off the lights or order all players to close their eyes tightly. The king of clubs makes believe to strike his victim with a knife, tapping him lightly. The victim shrieks and falls to the floor. Lights are turned on or the players are told to open their eyes. The jacks, told they are detectives, must find the murderer. They may ask not more than five questions of each player. All players but the murderer are warned that they must tell the truth. If the jacks do not detect the murderer he confesses and says, "I knew you'd never suspect me. It's in the cards."

FLYING SAUCERS

Use any number of the silver-paper covered plates on which one gets pies from the store. The opponents are at opposite ends of the gym. One team has the plates or flying saucers and throws them across the room at a given signal to the other team, whose members try to catch them. If, out of ten plates thrown, at least six are not caught the earth will be destroyed. Teams then change places.

REVERSE ACTION

Have two contestants who say the alphabet backward. One who finishes first without repetition or error wins. Do the same thing with Roman numbers from 100 to 1. If this last is too hard, as it probably will be, try something easy. See who can hold most marbles on the back of his hand, using any number of contestants.

CHICKEN RACE

Any number of contestants stand, feet together. They squat down low, their knees spread. Then arms are stretched out and their hands clasped in front of their legs below the knees. Then the contestants walk on their toes, with short steps, all around the room. The winner is the one who walks all around the room in the shortest time.

BUILD A BRIDGE

The players stand in a line about a foot apart, each holding a piece of chalk. They bend their knees, reach the right hand inside the right foot, between the legs, and chalk a mark on the floor as far forward as possible. Heels may be raised but the toes must not cross the line.

A PENNY A SPOON RACE

Have two contestants at a time. On the floor close to the starting line and just back of it, place two saucers each of which contains two pennies. At the finish line are two empty saucers, one for each contestant. Contestants are given a teaspoon which they must hold in the right hand, the left hand behind their back. Their toes are on the starting line. At a given signal each contestant bends over, scoops up a penny from a saucer, runs to the finish line and puts the penny in an empty saucer, runs back and repeats the performance with the other penny. If a penny is dropped, it must be picked up with the spoon and the race resumed. The one who finishes first and gets both pennies in the saucer at the finish line wins all four pennies.

MODERN BEN HURS

Have as many teams of three as desired or there is room for. There must be a starting point and a line at the end of the gym for the finishing line. The teams stand behind the starting line. Two representing horses stand in front, toes on the line. The driver is in the middle, close behind the horses. Handkerchiefs join the driver's hands with the outside hand of each horse. The starter drops a red handkerchief flag and each chariot runs to the finishing line and back. The driver must pass over the line as well as the horses. The horses may run, gallop, or skip, as decided beforehand.

ARE YOU IN CAHOOTS WITH ME?

This is an oldie. The Guesser is sent out of the room, and the others stand in a circle after placing any number of objects in the center of the circle. Objects should be varied—book, key, pencil, shoe, etc. Guesser is called in and handed a cane or wand. He asks, "Are you in cahoots with me?" They all say "Yes." Guesser then points to any object in the circle and asks, "Is it this?" They say "No" to every object he points to until he happens to say, "Is it that?" or "Is that it?" They say "No" to that also, but the object to which he points *after* using the word *that* in his question is the right one and the players say, "That's it. We're in cahoots with you."

INCHY-PINCHY—DON'T YOU LAUGH

This is another oldie. Players sit in a circle, all but one who, unknown to the others, has lampblack on his fingers. He walks around the circle, pinching each player on the cheek, and leaving a black smudge on the cheek of the first one pinched. As he walks around he repeats "Inchy-pinchy, don't you laugh!" The player with the smudge is not conscious of it. He is told to change places with the one who patted him. As he goes around patting the other players they naturally laugh at him, but he does not know why. He puts out anyone who laughs. After he has patted them all they tell him why they laughed.

RAP-A-TAP-TAP

The leader stands at the head of a line and has a cane in his right hand. He says, "Do as I do." He taps the cane three times and says, "Rap-a-tap-tap." Others all say, "Rap-a-tap-tap." The leader passes the cane to his left hand and gives it to the next in line who takes it in his right hand and says, "Rap-a-tap-tap." This is repeated down the line. The cane may be twirled, swung overhead, swung back and forth, put over his shoulder, dropped and picked up, anything desired, but it must be passed on with the left hand and taken by the right hand. Any player failing to do this is out of the game.

WHO CAN'T DO THIS?

The leader has a cane in his right hand. All stand in a circle. The leader taps the cane on the floor any number of times and says, "Who can't do this can't do much." He then changes the cane to his left hand and passes it on to the one on his left who is supposed to repeat the action. Any player failing to note the change of hands and passing cane on with right hand is put out but not told why. Most players concentrate on the number of taps which vary with each player. The object is to put out as many players as possible. No one but the leader can put a player out.

DROP YOUR MARBLES

A bottle or small can is on the floor at the right of the player. In his left hand he holds a bag of marbles. He takes them out, one at a time, holding it waist high, and tries to drop it into the bottle or can. The player dropping the most marbles into the receptacle in a given time wins.

HOLD UP YOUR HEAD

This is a race in which each player has on his head a cardboard box about a foot square. In the box is a tennis ball. The stunt is to see which one can walk the length of the room first without dropping the box. Hands must be clasped behind their backs.

DO WHAT I SAY

The players are in a semicircle and the leader stands where he can see them all. He tells them that a certain animal does something. If he is telling the truth and the animal really does what he says, the players are to do it. If it does not do what he says and the players do it, they are out of the game. The last player in wins. The leader might say, Geese fly, Donkeys bray, Elephants sing, Cows mew, etc.

BE AN AUTHOR

Letters of the alphabet, each written on a card, are put in a hat. Someone draws out three of the cards and announces which three letters are on them. Then each player, as rapidly as possible, must write three sentences, having been given paper and pencil before, and each sentence must begin with one of the three letters drawn, and each word in that sentence must begin with the same letter as the first word. Suppose the letters drawn are **B, J,** and **P.** You might get sentences like this:

Being bankrupt Ben borrowed Bill's big boat, bringing bacon back from Bermuda.

Jauntily jumping, Jane jiggled jugs, jingling jocosely.

Poor proud peacock, preening pertly, pending possible peril, picked peaches.

The individual wins who finishes the sentences first.

WHAT AM I SELLING?

From magazines and newspapers cut out slogans or parts of ads, being careful not to leave in the name of the product or its manufacturer. Paste these slogans on large sheets of paper and number each. Either pass them around or fasten them up on the wall. Players must guess the product advertised. The one guessing the most first wins. Answers should be written.

DON'T BE A BLOW-HARD

Have a collection of empty paper bags as nearly the same size as possible. Put them in a pile in the middle of the floor. The players are in two teams. When the leader, the same for both teams, says "Blow," the one at the right in each team rushes to the pile, picks up a bag, blows it up, bangs it and, as soon as the bag explodes, darts back to his place in line and taps the player at his left, who repeats the first player's performance. This continues until every player has burst a bag. The line that finishes first wins.

THE LOST LETTER

Cut any letter of the alphabet out of dark colored or black paper. Make the letter about an inch square. Send all but one of the guests from the room. Then place the letter, which no one has seen, on the dress or coat of the guest who remained in the room. It may be put in a lady's corsage, on a man's necktie, but never hidden as it must be in plain open sight. Call in the others and tell them you have lost an important letter and you wish them to help you find it. Explain that it is a letter from the alphabet, as soon as one person sees the letter he or she tells you in a whisper where it is and then sits down. The one who finds the letter last or not at all wins a booby prize.

BY-PASS

The two teams of players sit in two rows, facing each other, about six feet between the two rows. The stunt is to pass something from one end of the row to the other, each row passing the same sort of object. The winning team is, of course, the one passing the object down the row to the end first. If the object drops to the floor it is given back to the first player and the race starts all over again so far as that row is concerned.

A penny may be placed on the toe of the first player's left shoe, in which case no hands are used. This player moves his left foot past his neighbor's right foot to his left foot—the neighbor may draw in his right foot to facilitate the action—and lifts his own left foot so the coin will slide on his neighbor's shoe.

A baseball bat, held vertically, may be passed from right hand to the neighbor's right hand, a wet cake of soap, or a chestnut burr may be used if desired.

BOUNCING RACE

Have two strong heavy kitchen chairs and two competitors. Each stands at the back of his chair, bends over it, and grabs the sides of the chair at the bottom near the front. Then he moves the chair along the floor, jerking it to make it bounce. The winner is the one who moves his chair the greatest distance while the judge slowly counts to twenty.

SERVES YOU RIGHT FOR HAVING INITIALS

The leader prepares slips of paper bearing the initials of the players, numbers them and puts them in a box. Then each player draws a card. The first player stands up and reads the initials on his or her card and tells whose initials they are. Then the leader asks the other players questions about this person and each answer must be in words that begin with those initials. For example, the first player may see, reading from a card, "My name is Robert A. Turner. My initials are R. A. T." The leader may ask questions like this, "What is this person's reputation?" The answer might be, "Rude and tiresome." Leader asks, "How does he look?" Answer, "Ratty and tangled." Question, "Name his favorite pets." Answer, "Rabbits, anacondas, trout." Question, "How does he regard the fair sex?" Answer, "Robbie adores them." Question, "What does he think of the answers you're giving?" Answer, "Reckons ain't true." Question, "What do you think of him?" Answer, "Really ain't telling." And so on.

FOUR FROM FOUR

Tell the audience you are the only living person who can take four from four and leave eight. Then prove it by taking a square sheet of paper and tearing off the four corners, thus leaving eight corners.

AN ANGRY CHARADE

First the players crawl around on all fours, rapidly, like ants.

ANT

Next they play tag.   TAG

All say OH! loudly!   O

Each turns to his neighbor and strokes his head, scratches behind his ears, and moves the lips to form the words "Nize kitty."   NIZE

For the entire word two meet, push, appear to call each other names, pull hair, glare at each other.   One walks away, very angry.   Antagonize.

A PENNY IN THE POT

In the center of the floor have a tin pan or shallow pot, not too large.   Ask each guest to collect as many pennies as possible.   Then the players take turns kneeling at the extreme end of the room, opposite the pot, and tossing pennies, one at a time, into the pot.   Those that do not fall into the pot are gathered up and distributed among the contestants to be used again.   There is a scorekeeper, of course.   The one who puts the most pennies into the pot gets a prize, a dime or a quarter.   At the end of the game, put the money in a box and give to a charity.

GREETINGS

Each player, one at a time, greets another player or a member of the jury, which may consist of four judges. A prize is given for the most original or picturesque greeting and for the most insulting one. These greetings may range from "Howdy, pardner," "Hi, you bum," to "Hail, vision of loveliness."

WHO KNOWS

In an open doorway hangs a large sheet of very thick paper. Half of the players go back of the sheet in which a small hole has been cut. One of the players back of the sheet sticks his nose through the hole. The players outside guess whose nose it is. If someone guesses correctly, those back of the sheet clap their hands. If the guess is wrong they shout NO and another nose appears. If the guess was correct, the one whose nose was identified joins the guessers. After all noses have been seen the two groups change places.

A PERFECT FIGHT

Two boys are blindfolded and lie on the floor, rather far apart, facing each other. They grasp left hands firmly. Each has a folded newspaper in his right hand. At the word GO they try to strike each other with the newspaper. The one who gets in the most hits before the five minutes allowed is up wins the fight.

BEAT THE RAP

The leader has a gavel or a small hammer. He sits back of a table. The contestants, one at a time, pick up a dozen peanuts that have been thrown on the floor. Peanuts are still in their shells of course. A player starts to pick up peanuts at the word Go and stops at a rap of the gavel. All peanuts must be held in one hand. The player who picks up most peanuts wins. The score is kept and a new dozen peanuts are placed on the floor before another contestant starts. The winner is given all the peanuts and told to go feed the squirrels.

CORK IN THE BASIN

Fill a dishpan full of water for each contestant, preferably use two contestants at a time. Place four medium-sized corks in each pan. Each contestant tries to get the four corks out with his teeth, with his hands behind his back, before the other contestant can remove the corks from his pan.

ISN'T HE PRETTY?

Each woman makes up her male partner with cosmetics, lipstick, powder, rouge, etc., supplied by the hostess. The prettiest man, voted so by the group, wins the contest for the couple of which he is the unfortunate half.

JAIL BREAK

The player clasps his hands in front of his body and tries to step through the ring thus formed by his hands. He steps with left foot first and then with right foot, and must not unclasp his hands until he stands up straight again.

THE DANCING BEAR

Any number of couples are dancing. One man holds a huge teddy bear for a partner. He may cut in on any couple, giving the bear to the man. When the music stops the man holding the bear is out.

LIKE THE WORD SAYS

One player, the director, goes out and the others choose an adverb or an adjective. The director returns and asks the players to perform some act in the way of the word selected. Suppose the word chosen is quietly. The Director may say, "Walk like the word says." Players walk about quietly. He may say, "Look like the word says." They stand limp and expressionless as if sleepy. He may give five directions. If he does not guess the word by then he is out of the game or joins the players and another director is chosen.

THE FACE IS FAMILIAR

Cut from newspapers and magazines the faces of well-known or famous people. Paste each picture on a sheet of paper, number them, and fasten them on the wall as in an art gallery. Players are given a card and pencil and write down the names of the people in the pictures. The one having the most correct answers wins.

MADAM X

The players are told that in the room is the mysterious Madam X. The one who discovers her first will win a prize. Madam X has been chosen before the game begins, unknown to the others. Each player goes to the other guests, introduces himself and asks, "Are you Madam X?" Players do not take turns, but all start searching for Madam X at once. If she is discovered, she admits her identity.

UPSIDE DOWN RACE

Two contestants rest their bodies on their hands and heels, face upward, their backs to the floor, the body stiff and not sagging at the waist. They race to see who gets across the room first.

FILL UP THE ZOO

Players sit in a circle. At a signal the one chosen as the leader names an animal, the name of which starts with A. Moving to the right, the next player in the circle names an animal that starts with B—and so on through the alphabet. No names are to be repeated. There must not be more than 26 persons in the circle. Animals named may be: Aardvark, Bison, Cougar, Deer, Elephant, Frog, Goat, Horse, Ibex, Jackal, Kangaroo, Leopard, Mouse, Narwahl, Opossum, Panther, Quagga, Rhinoceros, Serpent, Tiger, Unicorn, Viper, Whale, Xema (a kind of gull), Yak, Zebra.

ZINGO
OR
WHO HAS THE KEY TO THE CLOTHES CLOSET?

The leader says this game will remind the players of Bingo because it is exactly the opposite. He hands each player a small piece of paper. Fastened to one piece is a small key. When he says "GO" players pass papers on from one to the other. When he calls "ZINGO" cards must all be held up. One having the card to which the key is attached is out. Papers are redistributed and game starts over again. The last person out wins.

KEEP OUT OF THE SWAMP

Players form in a circle, holding hands. On the floor, near to and inside the circle, three large red or green handkerchiefs are spread, far apart. To lively music the players prance around in a circle, keeping off the handkerchiefs, which are the swamps. Anyone getting even a toe in the swamp is out of the game. If one player can push another into the swamp it is allowed. When the music stops the winners are those who have kept out of the swamp.

FOLLOW THE SNAKE

Two groups form in two lines, each person, except of course the leaders, puts his hands about the waist of the person in front and must not let go. The last person in each line has a large handkerchief stuck in the back of his belt. To fast music or rapid counting the two lines follow their leaders who twist and turn, trying to snatch the opponent's tail, or handkerchief. The leader who accomplishes this, wins. When a snake line breaks all must stop and the game starts over again.

BACKWARD OR NOT

See who, in ten minutes, can write down the most three or four letter words that spell the same forward or backward, as Anna, boob, deed, sees, noon, dad, did, dud, etc.

THE MAD HATTERS

Get as many queer old hats as possible. Stand the players in a circle, each holding a hat. The leader counts. At 1 each player puts on his hat. At 2 he takes it off. At 3 he puts it on the head of the one at his right, and so on. When his own hat comes round to him again he takes it off and throws it in the center of a ring. When all hats are on the floor in the center the leader counts ten during which time each player must find his own hat and put it on. The last person to find his own hat is out.

A CORNY RACE

Have four glasses on a table, two empty ones and two filled with grains of dried corn. Have two people race to see which one, using one hand only and picking out grains one at a time, can transfer the corn grains from the full glass to the empty one first.

IN REVERSE

See who can in ten minutes write down the most words that when spelled backward make another word, as stop—pots, loot—tool, door—rood, live—evil, etc.

IT'S HOW YOU SAY IT

This is an excellent game to break the ice and make guests feel gay. Ask each person to repeat a familiar rhyme, such as "Little Jack Horner," "Mistress Mary Quite Contrary," or "A-Diller-A-Dollar," in a manner designated. For example, like an orator on the Fourth of July, like a tragedian, a comedian, a bashful child, an angry parent, one who lisps, one who is sad, one who is afraid, etc. Give a prize for the most entertaining version.

WALK A CHALK LINE

Draw a line on the floor or pin a white tape in a long straight line. Turn the contestant around rapidly half a dozen times. Put him at the head of the line and see if he can walk to the end without getting more than six inches off of the line.

HERE AND BACK AGAIN

Hold the left ear with the right hand and hold the nose with the left hand. As the leader counts one to ten the players repeat the action in reverse, holding the right ear with the left hand and the nose with the right hand. It isn't as easy as it sounds.

I HAD A LITTLE PONY

This is a race of couples. There must be a starting line and a finishing line. One player stands directly behind his running mate, both facing the course. At a signal from the starter the one behind jumps on the back of the one in front of him who carries him to the finish line and back to the starting line. If any part of the rider's body, such as his feet, touches the floor, he and his horse are disqualified.

SPELLING BEE

This is just like the traditional old-fashioned spelling bee except that all words must be spelled backward. The winner of course is the one who succeeds in spelling most words backwards. It is better if the one who gives out the words has then written down spelled backward.

WORDS IN WORDS

Players are given ten minutes in which to write down four-letter words containing other words, taking letters in regular order. For example, b-e-a-r contains be, ear, *Then* contains the-he-hen-en. The one who makes the most small words from the four letter words he has chosen wins.

TAKE A KNIFE

A blindfolded player has two dull table knives. The others move around him in a circle. When he clicks the knives together they stand still. Then any one player, at a signal from the others, steps out of the circle and up to the blindfolded one who feels of his face, not with fingers but with the knives, and tries to guess who it is. If he guesses correctly, they change places. If not, he tries again. Of course the person being examined keeps his eyes closed tightly, and the flat side of a knife, not the point, is used.

WHEEL THE BARREL

Take an empty sugar or flour barrel and put it on its side. Let contestants take turns standing on the barrel, balancing, and moving the barrel forward with their feet. Begin to count when both feet are on the barrel. The contestant who balances the longest and rolls the barrel the greatest distance before falling off is the winner.

PLANT YOUR GARDEN

This is the same as the Zoo game except that names of flowers or flowering bushes are used. For example: Azalea, Bluebell, Carnation, Daisy, Eglantine, Fuchsia, Gardenia, Honeysuckle, Iris, Jonquil, Kingcup, Lily, Marigold, Nasturtium, Oleander, Pansy, Quince, Rose, Tulip, U may be omitted, Violet, Wisteria, Omit X, Yarrow, Zinnia.

FORBIDDEN NUMBERS

Judge says to the players in a line, "You are to count, one at a time, from zero up to 100 but you must not mention any number divisible by 7, or including the number 7. If you do, you are out. The one who remains in the line the longest wins. If desired, the count may be up to 200, or may be repeated after 100 is reached.

EAT YOUR OATMEAL
OR
CORNFLAKES

Two boys, blindfolded, sit cross-legged on the floor, facing each other. Then each is given a bowl of oatmeal or cornflakes and a large spoon. He must feed his partner while his partner feeds him. The one who empties his bowl first wins.

FOOTSTEPS OF THE FAMOUS

The leader wears a mortarboard cap with a long tassel and has pinned on his coat many medals and ribbons, made of colored paper. The players form a line behind him and imitate his every movement. He may hop, skip, creep, crawl, jump, walk backward, whirl about, stand still, hold arms over his head, extend them forward, clap hands, anything he chooses. When he tires, he sits down abruptly on the floor and holds his hands to his head.

PAPER CUTTER

Give each player a large sheet of blank paper and a pair of scissors. In five minutes he must cut out something beautiful, amusing, or useful. Give a prize for the best cutting in each category.

THE ACROBATIC ANSWER MAN

If the contestant doesn't answer any question asked him promptly, he must do an acrobatic stunt, such as stand on his head, turn cart-wheels, anything designated by the other players. The questions asked should be absurd, such as: How high is up? Who is Sylvia? What is truth? How old is Ann? Why are hurricanes named after women? Why is the longest way round the shortest way home?

CAN YOU DO THIS?

Jump high into the air, slap both heels behind your back with your hands, jump up again and clap your feet together twice. Fold your arms in back of you, kneel on both knees and get up quickly without losing your balance and reach as high up as you can.

HOW COME? OR SOLVE THE MYSTERY

The player must give the solution to an absurd mystery told him by the leader. For example, the leader tells this: "The money was put into the safe. The safe was locked. Nobody knew the combination but Mr. Jones, whose money it was and who locked the safe. No one entered the house that night or nobody left the house. Next morning the safe was still locked but the money was gone. How come?"

Answer: Mr. Jones took the money out, of course.

TRY THIS

Try with your hands clasped behind your back, to hop on one foot around in a large circle.

THE WHISTLER

The player, blindfolded, must guess who is whistling an old familiar tune. He wins a prize if he guesses correctly. He may guess three times, a different tune being whistled each time. He must pay a forfeit if he misses all three times.

DRAW, PARTNER!

Each contestant is given a large sheet of paper, a pencil, and a card on which is named the subject he is to draw. After five minutes all papers are collected and tacked up so all may see. The picture judged the best by judges chosen from the audience wins a prize. Give the contestants crazy subjects, such as: A Lobster Waltzing; A Hurricane Trying to Decide Where to Go; etc.

FEATHER YOUR NEST

The contestants make as many words as possible from the letters in the word FEATHER, allowing five minutes from the time the papers are passed out until they are taken up.

THE POSTMAN

The leader calls the name of a player and says, "I have a letter for you." The leader names the letter— a letter of the alphabet. The player named must then name as many words as possible that begin and end with that letter. Suppose the letter given him is *a*. He might say: Anna, ana, Angora, agora, Atilla, Amanda, etc. The player naming the most words beginning and ending with a letter given him wins a prize. Do not give such letters as q, k, z, or y.

KEEP MOVING

Put five straight chairs in a row. The contestant sits in the last chair in the row. The leader asks her a question, any question. If the player answers correctly she moves up one chair. She is asked five questions in all. If she fails to answer a question correctly, she must move down one chair. Bible questions are suggested and may begin with easy ones and become more difficult. For example:

Who was the leader of David's choir? Asaph
What rose is mentioned in the Bible? Rose of Sharon
Name three kings who each reigned forty years. Saul, David, Solomon
To what hieroglyphics is the Rosetta Stone the key? Egyptian
Where is the Temple of Diana? Ephesus
Any player making the trip to the first chair wins a prize.

THE DAILY DOUBLE

Players are in a line or circle. The leader says, "Do what I do." He does many exercises, the sillier the better, and the players must do what he did twice. For example:—
1—Jumps up, claps hands.
2—Bows low.
3—Kneels and rises quickly.
4—Sneezes loudly.
5—Yells as if in pain.
6—Bites thumb.

DO AS I SAY

The leader gives directions rapidly to the players who stand in line.

1—Whirl, twirl, hurl.
2—At ease. Smile.
3—Attention. Walk, talk, gawk.
4—At ease. Frown.
5—Attention. Sigh, fly, cry.
6—At ease. Listen.
7—Attention. Call, haul, fall.
8—Get up. At ease.
9—Go home. You're all fired.

Directions should be carried out with exaggerated pantomiming.

LAP IT UP

Two contestants race, seeing which one can first empty a small saucer filled with milk by lapping it up like a cat.

DATE LINE

Ask the contestant to name at least three important dates and tell why they are important, in as short a time as possible. He may name 1066, 1492, 1775, and his birth date.

DON'T BE TOUCHY

The players march around the room to gay music. The leader calls a stop. He orders the players to touch something, such as "The tallest girl." They then march around until the leader gives another order, such as: "Touch your own toes," "Touch a bow tie," etc. End by something very silly: "Touch your weakest spot, your head."

WHAT WOULD YOU DO?

The players are in a line or a circle. Each player gives an answer to the player at his right, such as, "Bake five minutes," "Run to the police station," etc. The leader asks crazy questions of each player who must give the answer given him by his neighbor. For example, the leader asks, "What would you do if you lost your head?" The answer may be "Advertise for a new one." "What would you do if you were alone at midnight and heard a burglar down stairs?" "Wash my hair."

SPELLING BEE IN REVERSE

The contestants stand in line. The leader gives out words which must be spelled backwards. Those who miss must sit down. Begin with easy words, increase the difficulty. One who remains standing the longest wins.

A BONE TO PICK

Cut as many cardboard bones as there are players and number each one. Eleven is the lucky number. Each player draws a bone. The one having number eleven gives each of the others a stunt to do. After the stunts have been done, number eleven must do a stunt which the others decide upon. It must be difficult. A good one is to take a huge sheet of cardboard on which an enormous question mark has been drawn in black crayon. Under the question mark is a bone drawn on black. Number eleven is given a box of crayons and instructed to make a picture including the question mark and the bone in five minutes.

BUTTON UP YOUR OVERCOAT

The leader asks all the women to put on their coats and button them up. Those who fail to do so must pay a forfeit of twenty-five cents for some favorite charity. The women will usually button their coats down, beginning at the top.

ON YOUR KNEES, BOYS AND GALS

Two players interlace their fingers tightly. Each tries to force the other to his or her knees.

AREN'T YOU SLEEPY?

Stand before the group and yawn loudly and widely until all the others yawn. If, in a given time, two-thirds of the group are not yawning, the sleepy one has failed and must pay a forfeit.

ATTENTION! EYES FRONT

The leader pins a number on the back of each player who of course can not see his own number and is told not to turn his eyes from the front and so does not see the other numbers. At a given command, the players line up. The idea is to see how many players can get in a correct position before the specified time is up.

GOING AROUND IN CIRCLES

The players form in a single circle, holding hands. To any gay music they march around the room until the leader blows a whistle and gives orders for circle formations. For example: Make circles of four. The leader counts from one to five and then calls "Tally Ho." Those not in a circle of four stand in the center of the room till the next order, and get one black mark given by score keeper. Then a circle is again formed and the players march around as before. The leader gives other orders, circles of five, nine, etc., depending upon the number of players. When the leader is through, he calls: "Tally Ho. Make one big circle."

A NEW NUMBERS GAME

This is suitable for church socials. See who can answer correctly the most of these questions and answer them first. Tell the contestants each answer is a number. You might use these questions:

How many commandments? 10

How many apostles? 12

How many books in the Old Testament? 39

How many books in the New Testament? 29

How many books in the Bible begin with the letter T? 5—I Thessalonians, II Thessalonians, I Timothy, II Timothy, Titus.

For how many pieces of silver was Joseph sold? 20

How many children did Job have? 10

How many years did Job live? 140

When Moses, at the Lord's command, stretched forth his hand toward Heaven, for how many days was there darkness in the land of Egypt? 3

I DROPPED SOMETHING

Players are given paper and pencil. The leader stands behind a screen or curtain. At short intervals he drops ten different objects on the floor. The players must write the name of the object they think was dropped. If requested, the leader may drop an object a second time. The player having the most correct answers wins. Drop familiar objects such as a newspaper, a shoe, a bunch of keys, a spoon, a wet towel, a book, a bag of marbles, etc.

NUTS TO THE NUTTY

Suspend from the ceiling a paper sack of peanuts, shelled or not, on a strong cord. The sack should be from six to seven feet above the floor. Blindfold a player and have him swing at the sack with a stick or cane. The leader may swing the sack around to make the task of hitting it more difficult. When it is hit and bursts the one who hits it wins a prize. The one who gathers up the most peanuts from the floor wins another prize.

WATCH YOUR CARRIAGE

See who can carry the most things from one end of the room to the other. Take objects from the table on which have a strange assortment, and nothing with handles. Get objects that are difficult to carry.

THINK YOU CAN?

Have a number of pieces of paper, not too large, and bet the players they can't fold the piece they hold in half eight times. It sounds easy, but wait till you try it!

BIBLICAL HISTORY TEST

Choose any number of men and women to represent a well-known Biblical character each. They tell three things about themselves and the players guess the identity, one guess to each player. Any character whose name is not guessed collects a dime from each player for charity. A person portraying Absalom might say, "I had a beautiful sister. I was the son of a king. I was slain in an oak tree."

THE BRAMBLE BUSH

To the tune of "The Mulberry Bush" the players move around in a circle. The leader is in the center. When the leader raises his hands the players stand still. Beginning with the one at whom the leader points, each player must immediately name a bush. Moving around the circle from the left to right, each player does the same. No repetitions.

UNLUCKY NUMBERS

Write numbers 1 to 50 on small cards, drop them into a hat, and have each player draw a card. Those drawing cards with number 7, 11, 13, or 23 must do any stunt the others decide upon.

THE $64,000,000 QUESTION

Seat the players in a circle. Beginning with one chosen by the leader, each player asks the one at his left any question he wishes. The question is supposed to be answered truthfully and without hesitation. The one giving the best answer and the one asking the best question win a prize each. The leader is the judge. The crazier the questions the better.

WHO IS IT?

The victim chosen must describe any famous person or anyone in the room, mentioning no names but being as flattering or as derogatory as he wishes. If the audience guesses the person described, the victim must continue describing persons until he gets one the audience can not guess.

WHO'S MISSING?

The leader names a famous person in fact or fiction who had a well-known companion. The player called upon must give this companion's name. If no one can guess who it is, the leader tells the name and gives another celebrity with a famous pal. For example: Sherlock Holmes and Watson; Antony and Cleopatra; Pat and Mike; Mary and Martha, or the lamb; Lion and Androcles; etc.

ONE FOR THE BIRDS

Each player has pinned to his back the name of a bird. He must find out by questioning the others what bird he is. He is permitted ten questions only. When he thinks he has learned his name he tells the leader. If correct, he steps out of the game. When all have asked the ten questions, those who learned their names inflict a penalty on those who did not. Penalties must be connected with birds, such as: Walk like a penguin; Bill and coo like a pigeon; Choosing your partner; Sing like a lark; Hoot like an owl.

BEAT THE RAP

The leader sits at the table with a gavel. He asks the victim to name ten of anything specified before he, the leader, raps on the table. He may ask the victim to name ten explorers, radio programs, minerals, inventors, fish, etc. He will be given a very short time in which to name them.

CHAMPION WEIGHT LIFTER

Challenge anyone to lift as big a weight as you can. Have on the table, assorted weights, some light, some heavy. When the contestants have finished you bring forth and hold up a huge sheet of white cardboard on which is printed in enormous letters the word, W-A-I-T.

FOLLOW THE MUSIC

The guests stand in a circle. Music of old games that were once very popular with children is played and the guests must play the game. The music is changed frequently and abruptly and the guests must change their movements to fit the music. Suggested games are:

Here We Go Round the Mulberry Bush; A-Tisket-A-Tasket; Go In and Out the Window; Farmer in the Dell; Did You Ever See a Lassie; Looby Loo; London Bridge; Ring-around-a-Rosie.

SIDEWAYS RELAY RACE

The couples stand back to back, elbows locked together, on the starting line. At the signal they run, sideways, to the goal or the finish line.

THE RHYMERS

The leader starts the game by giving a word to the first person in a circle, who must give a word that rhymes with it. The next person gives a word to the player next to him who must give a word that rhymes, and so on around the circle. Use hard words, such as: squaw, flutter, steeple, chasm, story, vanish, etc.

SOMETHING NEW FOR DINNER

The players are given pencils. A long sheet of paper is handed to the first player who is told to write the name of a delicious new dish, a recipe for which is about to be written. Then the paper is folded over and handed to the next in line who writes down an ingredient or direction, and so on, around the circle. When all have written something, the recipe is read aloud by the leader. Something like this is usually the result.

Salamander Souffle

Take two cups kerosene
Wings of four grasshoppers
One quart molasses
A pinch of sodium sulphate
Three hard-boiled eggs, unshelled
Skins of a dozen baked potatoes
A bottle of nail polish
Six ice cubes
Half a bottle of soda mints
A pound of ground chicken bones
Dust with rye flour
Bake in slow oven for two days
Ice with suntan lotion
Throw in garbage can.

WHOSE HOO?

Someone is blindfolded. Others stand in a circle, the blindfolded one in the center, and hoot like an owl. The blindfolded one tries to identify the hooter.

WHAT IS THIS?

The leader points to his hand and says, "This is my hand," and counts quickly to ten. Other players touch the nose, foot, anything but the hand and say, "This is my hand." Keep this up until some player touches what the leader touched. He is out and must be the leader.

ACTION SPELLING

The leader gives the rules. For each vowel in a word spelled, the players clap their hands twice. For consonants, clap the hands once. A scorekeeper eliminates those who make mistakes.

REVERSE ENGLISH

The leader gives orders to the players who are sitting in a row. The players do what is ordered but in reverse:

a—Sit still. (Players stand up)
b—Jump up. (Players sit)
c—Count from 1 to 10. (Count from 10 to 1)
d—Say farewell. (Say hello)
e—Go to sleep. (Stand up and dance)
f—Be very quiet. (Talk—whistle—sing)
g—Call your dog. (Yell SCAT)
h—Sing a gay song. (Weep)

THINK FAST OR OUT YOU GO

This is suitable for a church party. The players sit in a circle. The questioner stands in the center of the circle. He announces, "You! The person at whom I point, must answer the question correctly at once or out you go." He asks questions about the Bible. If not answered correctly and at once, the person called upon leaves the circle. Another question is asked. The one missed is not repeated as other players may have had time to think of the answer. Make some of the questions hard. Here are a few:

1—Name three precious stones mentioned in the Bible. Diamond, ruby, pearl.
2—Name three musical instruments mentioned in the Bible. Harp, trumpet, viol.
3—Name three Biblical characters with whom God made a covenant. Noah, Abraham, Isaac, Jacob, David.
4—Name three birds mentioned in the Bible. Raven, dove, stork.
5—Give three other names for the Devil. Satan, Apollyon, Beelzebub.
6—What Biblical character invented music, and was father "of all such as handled the harp or the organ"? Jubal
7—How many vials were made of gold and filled with the wrath of God as told in Revelations? Seven
8—What insect was used as food in Biblical times? Locust
9—Where in the Bible is a mortgage mentioned? Nehemiah 5-3. "We have mortgaged our lands . . . that we may buy corn."
10—Name three uses of oil in Bible times. In lamos, for anointing, rubbed on meat offerings.

SLAP HAPPY

Players sit in a circle. Each one takes the name of an emotion or feeling, as sad, happy, solemn. One must be happy. There must be no repetition of names. One player who has been out of the room is called in. Players in a circle try to look the opposite of the emotion they have chosen as name. The sad ones look glad, etc. The player brought in is told to prove that he is a slaphappy chap by slapping Happy, one of the persons in the circle. If after three trials he does not succeed in slapping the right person he must pay a fine.

WHAT'S IN A NAME?

One person is sent out of the room and he is given a name by the others. When he is called in he is told four facts about himself and his name. If he fails to guess his name he pays a forfeit.

You are a famous animal. **Mickey (mouse)**.

You are an undesirable drink. **Mickey (Finn)**.

You are a movie actor. **Mickey (Rooney)**.

You are the author of famous detective stories. **Mickey (Spillane)**.

You are a nursery rhyme heroine. **Sally (Waters)**.

You are a sudden attack in war. **Sally**.

You are a tea cake. **Sally (Lunn)**.

You are used in baking. **Saleratus Sally (ratus)**.

DOG DAYS

The same procedure as above, only **use words** beginning with letters **D-O-G**.

A STUNT TO END ALL STUNTS

Ask each player or guest to write on a slip of paper the most difficult stunt he can think of. Give each player a number to put on his slip. Have a copy of each player's number. Correct and shuffle the slips, then gather them up so you, only, can see the numbers and give each player back his own slip, telling him that is the stunt he is to do.

SEA, AIR, LAND, OR NOWHERE?

The person having to pay a forfeit must answer 9 out of 10 questions correctly. The following names are suggested:

Did these people win their fame on sea, air, land, or nowhere?

Columbus, Lindbergh, any player, the man with the hoe, Hudson, the trapeze performer, Pocahontas, Captain Nemo, Three Wise Men of Gotham, Wild Bill Hickok, Martin Luther, Noah, etc.

POP THE QUESTION

The player must answer before the leader counts to ten and give the definition of words beginning with p-o-p.

A talkative coxcomb. **POPinjay.**
A kind of tree. **POPlar.**
A corded fabric. **POPlin.**
Something good to eat. **POPover.**
A gay flower. **POPpy.**
Approved by the people. **POPular.**

PROVERB GAME

This is for adults. One person is sent from the room. The others select a proverb. When the guesser returns he is told how many words there are in the proverb. He is to ask questions and each answer he gets will contain a word in the proverb, in its order—the first word in the first answer, etc. If he does not guess the proverb after he has asked as many questions as there are words in the proverb he must start all over again, the first answer containing the first word of proverb, as before. Suppose the proverb chosen is A STITCH IN TIME SAVES NINE. The action might go like this:

Question: When did this happen? Answer: On a clear day. **A.**

Question: Is it sad or funny? Answer: Funny. I laughed till I got a stitch in my side. **Stitch.**

Question: Where did the people live? Answer: In the country, I think. **In.**

Question: Is this a well-known proverb? Answer: Yes. It should take you a very short time to answer it. **Time.**

Question: Do you do what the proverb says? Answer: No, but my mother saves proverbs for me to read. **Saves.**

Question: Is this proverb connected with a famous story, like Cinderella? Answer: No, nor it isn't about the nine tailors, either. **Nine.**

THROW IN THE TOWEL

Two contestants, one at a time, the other out of the room, name as many movie actors or actresses as possible while the leader counts to ten. They may name states in the union, cities in Europe, shade trees, etc.

DO YOUR STUFF

The contestants come before the audience one at a time, none knowing what those preceding him have done. The leader gives them the stunt before they enter, and all are given the same stunt. Judges award a prize to the best portrayal. They may be asked to do imitations of—a cat on a hot tin roof, a snake in the grass, a mouse in a trap, a fly in the ointment, a dog in the manger, etc.

THIS IS IT

The guests must decide what is represented by the five players, each of whom impersonates the same thing but in a different manner. Five guesses may be allowed. Suppose players have decided upon a fisherman as their subject. The first one may, in pantomime, dig worms; the second picks up an imaginary basket and pole; the third sits on bank of a stream and casts his line; the fourth gets a bite but the fish gets away; the fifth, tired out, lies down and sleeps. A cook may be represented, like this: First one gathers up material; second sifts flour; third breaks eggs in a bowl; fourth stirs a mixture, puts it in a pan and then into the oven; fifth takes cake out of the oven, cuts a slice, eats it.

FOLLOW ME

This resembles Step This Way but players are in a line back of the leader who announces what he is going to do. They must imitate his actions. For example he may say: "I'm climbing a mountain, follow me," etc. He may swim the English Channel; run in a track meet; do a pole vault; ride a bucking pony; drop in a parachute; fight a duel with a sword; meet an old friend; figure his income tax; row in a boat race, etc.

BE A MAGICIAN

Tell the audience you are going to put yourself through the key hole of the door. Have those who doubt you stand on the other side of the door, close the door, write the word MYSELF on a slip of paper, roll the slip up and push it through the keyhole. Then open the door, pick up the paper and say, "See? It says MYSELF on the paper. I put myself through the keyhole."

BACKWARD

Tell the audience you can recite a poem backward as rapidly and as accurately as in the usual manner. If they doubt your ability, just turn your back to the audience and recite a poem.

KEEP YOUR BALANCE

Balance a feather on your nose and clap your hands together at the same time.

RUN A MILE

This is an oral test.   Each contestant is asked five questions, and moves a mile for each correct answer. He takes five steps forward to indicate the miles gained. The questions may be difficult and sensible or silly and easy.   If contestant does not answer he is told the correct one, or a silly one, and must sit down.   The winner is one who walks five miles.   Of course any amusing answer may be accepted.   Here are a few questions and answers.

What is doggerel?   **A little dog.**

What is an autobiography?   **The story of motor cars.**

What is an optimist?   **An eye doctor.**

What is a caboose?   **An Indian baby.**

What is a pomegranate?   **A lap dog.**

Who is the most famous runner?   **Adam, first in the human race.**

When is your doctor angry?   **When he loses his patients.**

When is a room full of people empty?   **When the folks are all married and there's not a single person in the room.**

What musical instrument can never be believed?   **A lyre.**

How can I stop snoring?   I snore so loudly I wake myself up.   **Just sleep in the next room.**

If I give one boy ten cents and another fifteen cents what time is it?   **A quarter to two.**

KEYS

One is a prisoner; he sits in chair tied by paper chains. He must find ten keys before he can be free. This is done by guessing the word defined or mentioned in the sentence (Though not by name) and beginning or ending with the word KEY, or its sound. For example, someone says: "I walked under this the rainy day I went to the theater." **Marquee.**

MATCHING PROVERBS

A GAME FOR ADULTS OR CHILDREN

Old and well-known proverbs are printed on paper and the paper is then cut into halves or thirds, leaving a portion of the proverb on each piece of paper. These pieces are shuffled and distributed among the guests. They have ten minutes in which to find other parts of proverb and re-assemble them. When this is done the players will be in groups of two or three. The last group to finish wins a booby prize.

I—YOU—HER—HIM

Each player is given ten small cardboard circles representing dimes. They ask questions of each other and collect a dime from anyone who, in answering the question, uses the word I, you, her, or him. The questions are of course designed to make the use of one of the words essential. One with most dimes after the given time is up wins prize. Answerers are not told words they must not use, if game is to be difficult.

CELEBRITIES—A PENNY APIECE

The leader points at a player and asks a question about a famous person. If he does not get a correct answer immediately, the player who fails to answer must drop a penny into a jar. One dropping no pennies wins a prize. Ask both easy and difficult questions, such as:

Who proved you can't keep a good man down? **Jonah.**
Whose favorite weapon was a sling shot? **David.**
Who owed his life to a thorn? **Androcles.**
What famous statesman has a nickname like the Pooh? **Winnie—Churchill.**
What woman owes her fame to work with a needle? **Betsy Ross.**
What maiden raked hay on a summer's day? **Maud Muller.**
Who was the first Earl of Chatham? **William Pitt.**
What captain had his guests come on board by twos? **Noah.**
Who wanted people to eat cake? **Marie Antoinette.**
Who got into trouble by looking backward? **Lot's wife.**

STEP THIS WAY

Pick two contestants and give a prize to the one who, in the eyes of the judges, most accurately follows the orders given by the leader. Orders should be difficult and confusing. Step like a playful kitten; like a giant; a ghost; a man with a sore toe; a woman with shoes too small; a pigeon on a chimney; a child going to school; a child coming home from school; a kangaroo · a cowboy who has been riding his horse all day.

WORD TEAMS

A player gives a word. Some one else must give a team word, such as ready-cash; pink-elephant; dark-horse; shaggy-dog; big-business. Anyone who fails to get an answer to the word he names wins.

YOUR SENTENCE

The players sit in a circle. The first person gives a word beginning with A, the next with B, etc., through the alphabet, but words must make sense—and constitute a sentence. Amy bought Clara dark elegant fur glockenspiels hoping insanely John King, like many nice old poets, quite relentlessly sees them understanding vindictively whose xylophone yaps zestfully.

THE CAT'S MEOW

This is a written test on vocabulary. The leader says: "Name the cats." She defines the word which begins with the letters C-A-T, and the players write a word. Use any word in the dictionary, such as catacombs, catechism, catnip, category, catalepsy, catastrophe, etc.

WHO SAID IT?
A QUIZ FOR ADULTS

The leader asks questions. The player who answers the most questions correctly wins a prize. The quiz may be written if desired.

1. Our Federal Union; it must be preserved. **Andrew Jackson.**

2. My God hath sent His angel, and hath shut the lions' mouths. **Daniel.**

3. Do not count your chickens before they are hatched. **Aesop.**

4. Knowledge is power. **Francis Bacon.**

5. It is better to know nothing than to know what ain't so. **Josh Billings.**

6. But where shall wisdom be found, and where is the place of understanding? **Job.**

7. God's in his heaven; all's right with the world. **Browning.**

9. The groves were God's first temples. **Bryant.**

10. I would rather be right than be president. **Clay.**

11. Justice is truth in action. **Disraeli.**

12. God helps those that help themselves. **Franklin.**

13. Let us have faith that right makes might and in that faith let us to the end dare to do our duty as we understand it. **Lincoln.**

14. To travel hopefully is a better thing than to arrive. **R. L. Stevenson.**

15. Knowledge comes but wisdom lingers. **Tennyson.**

16. 'Tis heaven alone that is given away;
   'Tis only God may be had for the asking. **Lowell.**

17. Wings for the angels but feet for the men. **Holland.**

18. We have nothing to fear but fear itself. **F. D. Roosevelt.**

19. The fog comes on little cat feet. **Carl Sandburg.**
20. Oh, it's home again, and home again, America for me! **Henry VanDyke.**
21. But trailing clouds of glory do we come
    From God who is our home. **Wordsworth.**
22. And if light is, it is because God said, "Let there be light." **Rossetti.**
23. Eternal Spirit of the chainless Mind. **Byron.**
24. A thing of beauty is a joy forever. **Keats.**
25. O, yet we trust that somehow good
    Will be the final goal of ill. **Tennyson.**

HORRORS

To play the game of HORRORS, the guests are arranged in groups of four and the first in each group is given a large piece of white drawing paper. Pencils or colored crayons may be given to all. Number one draws a face, folds the paper over, gives it to number two who draws arms and body. Folds and gives it to three who draws legs. Number four draws the feet. The object is to make each part of the picture as ghastly as possible. Most horrible drawing wins a prize.

THREE IN ONE

The contestants are told to do three improbable things all at once, as imitating a horse, a cat, and a dog. (He can gallop, claw and bark.)

Imitate a cow, a traffic cop and a whistler.

Imitate a soldier, a singer and a boxer.

BIBLICAL ALPHABET

There are two teams. The stunt is to name a Biblical character, beginning with A—down the alphabet, ending with Z—using letters in order. The team that misses the fewest names wins. We go from Adam to Zebediah. Team one begins and team two must not use any name used by team one. In place of people, animals named in the Bible may be mentioned, or places. Certain letters will of course have to be omitted.

WHERE DO YOU LIVE?

All are seated in a circle. Each one announces the name of a city he has chosen. One player, blindfolded, stands in the center of the circle. The leader, not in the circle, calls out names of two cities—Boston, Chicago,—and the players with those names change places as one in the center tries to touch one or get a chair.

TELEGRAMS

The players all have paper and pencil. On each paper ten letters are written, far enough apart for words to be inserted. Each player must write a telegram in which words begin with the letters on the paper, in the order given. For example: if the letters are S-D-E-G-K-U-P-S-M-Y—Telegram might read: Send dozen eggs. Going kitchen. Ulcers pain. Soon must yell. After telegrams are done pass to the right and have each player read his neighbor's message.

BE A POET

All have paper and pencil. Each writes an original line of verse, folds the paper over, passes it to the neighbor on the right and tells him the last word of the line. The second player writes a second line, rhyming with the first; folds the paper over and passes it on, telling the word with which the next line must rhyme, and so on, around the circle, which should not be too large. Then start over again. When the game is done there will be as many poems as there are players on the circle. Poems are then read aloud. Here is one:

> Mary had a little cat
> Who played at baseball with a rat.
> This little pig grew very fat.
> I conked my brother with a bat.
> She bought the hen a new red hat.
> The broom is riding on the mat.
> My mother likes to knit and tat.

OPINIONS DIFFER

This is an amusing oral stunt. Have two teams, seated, facing each other. The first team praises; the second team slurs. The letters of the alphabet are used in order to describe any desired thing. For example, an imaginary hostess. The first person on the first team says: "She is admirable." The first person on the second team says: "She is abominable," and so on, using all letters.

MUSIC USED IN THE BOOK

SONGS FROM "SONGS WORTH WHILE," T. S. DENISON & COMPANY, PUBLISHERS, MINNEAPOLIS.

Annie Laurie
Believe Me, If All Those Endearing Young Charms
Bluebells of Scotland
Bonnie Doon
Boola Song
The Campbells are Comin'
Come Back to Erin
De Camptown Races
Darling Nelly Gray
Dem Golden Slippers
The Dutch Warbler
Hail, Hail, the Gang's All Here
Home, Sweet Home
Jingle, Bells
Killarney
La Paloma
Long, Long Ago
Merrily, Merrily (round)
Old Zip Coon (music of Turkey in the Straw)
Polly-Wolly-Doodle
Scotland's Burning (round)
Swanee River
Twinkle, Twinkle, Little Star
The Wearing of the Green

MUSIC FROM "DENISON'S DESCRIPTIVE MUSIC BOOK," T. S. DENISON & COMPANY, PUBLISHERS, MINNEAPOLIS.

For He's a Jolly Good Fellow
Flower Song
Amaryllis
Moment Musical
Spring Song (Mendelssohn)
Traumerei
Wedding March, from Mendelssohn's "Midsummer Night's Dream"
Funeral March (Chopin)

SONGS FROM "THE GOLDEN BOOK OF FAVORITE SONGS," HALL & MCCREARY, PUBLISHERS, CHICAGO.

All Through the Night
Anvil Chorus, from "Il Trovatore"
Hail to the Chief
The Heart Bowed Down, from Balfe's "Bohemian Girl"

Keep the Home Fires Burning
Loch Lomond
Onward, Christian Soldiers (also in any hymnal)

OTHER SONG BOOKS AND SHEET MUSIC
Country Gardens (Grainger)—G. Schirmer, Inc., Publishers, New York
Let's Take an Old-Fashioned Walk—Irving Berlin Music Publishing Co., New York
Come, Ye Thankful People—any hymnal
You're the Flower of My Heart (Sweet Adeline)—M. Witmark & Sons, Publishers, New York
Over the River and Through the Wood (Thanksgiving Day)—in "Second Year Music Book," American Book Co., Publisher, New York.

RECORDS

On Parade (played by Goldman Band)—Columbia record 36038
High Ridin' (played by Goldman Band)—Columbia record 36167
National Emblem March (ditto)—Columbia record 35907
Glowworm (Glinka)—Columbia record 305-M
Three O'Clock in the Morning (Terriss-Robledo)—Columbia record 35619
Home on the Range (Guion)—Victor record 10-1273
The Lost Chord (Sullivan)—Columbia record 36812
School Days (Cobb-Edwards)—Victor record 24178
Somewhere a Voice Is Calling (Newton-Tate)—Victor album P 163
Overture to "William Tell" (Rossini)—Columbia record 35299
Golliwog's Cakewalk (Debussy)—Columbia record 395-M
Anvil Chorus, from "Il Trovatore"—Columbia record 7307-M
Indian Love Call (Friml)—Columbia record 36200
When the Moon Comes Over the Mountain (sung by Kate Smith)—Columbia record 36045
Give Me Something to Remember You By (Schwartz)—Columbia record 36578
You Forgot to Remember (Berlin)—Victor record album P-159
Dance of the Hours (Ponchielli)—Victor record 11833
Smiles (old song)—Columbia record 36701
Amaryllis (Seredy)—Victor record 20169
Easter Parade (Berlin)—Victor record 20-1566
A Bicycle Built for Two, or Daisy Bell (Lake)—Victor record 4395
Beautiful Blue Danube Waltz (Strauss)—Columbia record 35416
Let's Take an Old-Fashioned Walk (Berlin)—Columbia record 20-3469

Missouri Waltz (played by Goodman)—Columbia record 35617
Melody in F (Rubinstein)—Columbia record 71464-D
The Muffin Man—Victor record 20806
Little Gray Home in the West—Columbia record 36218
Ol' Man River (Kern)—Columbia record 35757
Bridal Chorus from "Lohengrin" (Wagner)—Columbia record
    7271-M
Turkey in the Straw—Columbia record 35784
Sidewalks of New York—Victor record 27380
Narcissus (Nevin)—Victor record 20443
Spring Song (Mendelssohn)—Columbia record 410-M
A Bird in a Gilded Cage—Columbia record 35807
Mandalay—Victor record 11877
Moonglow (Hudson)—Victor record 27405
Moonlight Sonata (Beethoven)—Victor record 16250
Prisoner's Song (Massey)—Victor album C-28
Barnum and Bailey's Favorite—Columbia record 36167
Smoke Gets in Your Eyes (Kern) (harmonica solo)—Columbia
    record 35516
Finlandia (Sibelius)—Columbia record 11178-D
Ciribiribin—Columbia record 35316
Don't Fence Me In—Columbia record 36761
Sleeping Beauty Waltz (Tchaikovsky)—Columbia record 35549
Pilgrims' Chorus, from "Tannhäuser" (Wagner)—Columbia record
    7271-M
I Love You Truly (Bond)—Victor record 24806
Love's Old Sweet Song (Molloy)—Columbia record 36811
Can't Help Lovin' That Man (Kern)—Columbia record 55005
Minuet (Boccherini)—Columbia record 70674-D
Dance of the Comedians (Smetana)—Columbia record 12210-D
Liberty Bell March (Sousa)—Columbia record 366-M
Over the Waves—Columbia record 36491
Danse Macabre (Saint-Saëns)—Columbia record 11251-D
Santa Claus Is Coming to Town—Columbia record 35786
The Stars and Stripes Forever (Sousa)—Columbia record 35907
Dancing Doll (Poldini)—Columbia record 71307-D
Cornet Chop Suey (cornet solo by Armstrong)—Columbia record
    36154
March of the Little Fauns (Pierne)—Columbia record 395-M
March Militaire (Schubert)—Columbia record 35719
Coronation March (Meyerbeer)—Columbia record 7331-M
My Heart Stood Still (Rodgers)—Columbia record 36476
Chinese Dance, from "Nutcracker Suite" (Tchaikovsky)—Colum-
    bia record 69800
Toreador's Song, from "Carmen" (Bizet)—Columbia record
    71681-D

The Last Round-up (Hill)—Victor record 10-1273
Humoresque (Dvorak)—Columbia record 17337-D
Semper Fidelis March (Sousa)—Columbia record 36038
Sextette, from "Lucia di Lammermoor" (Donizetti)—Columbia
   record 7180-M
Ride, Tenderfoot, Ride—Columbia record 35797
Oh, Susannah (Foster)—Victor record 4569
Anchors Aweigh—Columbia record 366-M
Bell-Bottom Trousers—Columbia record 36801
Sailor's Hornpipe—Victor record 21685
March of the Toys (Herbert)—Columbia record 7364-M

My Melancholy Baby (Burnett)—Victor record 25473
Serenade (Drigo)—Victor record 1538
Merry Widow Waltz (Lehar)—Columbia record 36086
Star Dust (Carmichael)—Victor record 20-1754
Under the Double Eagle March (Wagner)—Columbia record
   4238-M